ACHARYADEVO BHAVA & SNEHA
Story Work Book

JET Publisning House

INDIA   USA

TOWARDS EXCELLENCE

P
R
A
J
N
A

Title	Acharyadevo Bhava & Sneha
Subtitle	Story Work Book
Copyright	Jeeyar Educational Trust
First Edition	2012
Contributor	His Holiness Chinna Jeeyar Swamiji

CONTACT US:

INDIA	**UNITED STATES**
JIVA Sriramanagaram, Shamshabad, R.R. Dist. Andhra Pradesh - 509 325 Phone: 95535 49971, 95535 499	JETUSA Inc. Jeeyar Asram, 222, Dey Road, CRANBURY, NJ 08512, USA Phone:609-297-8797

Website: www.prajna4me.org   **Email:** prajna@jetusa.org

A Word

Dear friends !

There are four variables that influence man to become good or otherwise - mother, father, teachers, and friends. These four factors have tremendous impact right from the early stages of life. The positive influence of them molds man to become a good citizen to serve his society well.

We do not choose our parents. They are God's gifts to us. As we have learned in Module 2, mother and father are worthy of worship equal to God. We were hom only out of their grace. Ve:da also told us, "ma:thrude:vo: bhava" and "pithrude:vo: bhava", thereby recognizing their importance in shaping a child's personality.

However, as the child grows, curiosity to explore and learn about the world around grows too. Up to a certain stage, parents foster this curiosity, and provide the child the basics. However, as the curiosity increases, a child needs other sources to appease it. As a result, teachers and friends come into play. Because teachers and friends are chosen based on our own discretion, choosing the right ones is essential for a child's proper development and growth. Therefore, *'a:cha:ryade:vo: bhava'* and *'sne:ham'* are the central themes of Module 3.

A teacher is one who imparts knowledge to a seeking student. But it is important to make sure that the mentor is qualified, and that the education he imparts is efficient. With both of these, the teacher becomes a good teacher. By choosing the right mentors, we will be able to get good knowledge, and get to know the truths of the world.

A man is who his friends are. His personality is the reflection of his friends'. If a man is surrounded by good friends, he is positively influenced by them. As a result, he becomes a good person. However, if a man mingles with people who have questionable tendencies, his own personality changes to reflect that. The fragrance of a flower lingers on our clothes as we continue to wear it. Similarly, the fragrance of good friendship shows its impact on our life as we continue to maintain it. In addition, wise men always assess us based on our friendships. The company of bad people always ruins our image.

A guru, his tutelage, and the friendships we make play a pivotal role in further developing a child's personality. Knowing this is important. Hence, we have chosen these topics for discussion and study in Module 3. Elaborating the story is not our purpose. Our purpose is to make sure the students to understand the spirit of the story. We want to drive home the point of each lesson for the user to grasp its essence and apply it in his own life. However, we have tried our best to stay authentic to the stories.

We offer our mangalasasanams to everyone who worked carefully to put together the contents of this book, the artists who drew beautiful pictures to illustrate the story though the time was short, and the contributors of the workbook who created stimulating exercises for the benefit of the students. Users are always welcome to provide feedback with suggestions on its improvement.

PRAJNA PLEDGE

Jai Srimannarayana!

O Mother Earth! I, being your best child and responsible citizen of this world, take this pledge!

I shall revere my parents, my family, my Gurus and treat everyone with love.

I shell serve my community, my country and those in need.

I pledge to protect the Nature by caring for animals, trees and the environment.

I will learn from the experiences of my ancestors and pass it on to future generations.

I, as student of Prajna, swear to abide by the universal commandments.

Worship your own and Respect all & Serve all beings as service to God.

Jai Srimannarayana!

CONTENTS

A:CHA:RYADE:VO:BHAVA

SNE:HA

YO:GA:SANA:S

Telugu	Hindi	English		Telugu	Hindi	English
అ	अ	a		ట	द	ta
ఆ	आ	a:		ఠ	ठ	tta
ఇ	इ	i		డ	ट	**tta**
ఈ	ई	i:		ఢ	ड	**da**
ఉ	उ	u		ణ	ढ	**dda**
ఊ	ऊ	u:		ణ	ह	**dha**
ఋ	ऋ	ru		ణ	ण	**na**
ౠ	ॠ	ru:		త	त	tha
ఌ	अलृ	lu		త్త	त्त	ththa
ౡ	अलॄ	lu:		● థ	स्थ	} ttha
ఎ		e		●● థ	थ	
ఏ	ए	e:		ద	द	da
ఐ	ऐ	ai		ద్ద	द्द	dda
ఒ		o		ధ	ध	dha
ఓ	ओ	o:		న	न	na
ఔ	औ	au/ow		ప	प	pa
అం	अं	am		ఫ	फ	pha
అః	अः	aha		బ	ब	ba
క	क	ka		భ	भ	bha
ఖ	ख	kha		మ	म	ma
గ	ग	ga		య	य	ya
ఘ	घ	gha		ర	र	ra
ఙ	ङ	nga		ల	ल	la
చ	च	cha		వ	व	va
ఛ	च	chcha		శ	श	sa
● ఛ	छ	} chha		ష	ष	sha
●● ఛ	छ			స	स	sa
జ	ज	ja		హ	ह	ha
ఝ	झ	jha		ళ	ळ	la
ఞ	ञ	ini		ఱ		rra
				క్ష	क्ष	ksha
				జ్ఞ		Jna

● This letter comes only in the middle of the word

● ● This letter comes in the beginning/middle of the word

☞ Pronounciation of both these letters is almost similar

Jai Srimannarayana!

1. INTRODUCTION

I. Choose the Correct Answer

1. Parents
      a. are the last gurus
      b. build castles
      c. build schools
      d. give knowledge

2. A:cha:rya
      a. unfolds inner knowledge
      b. gives fruits
      c. goes to office
      d. prints books

3. Knowledge has
      a. 3 levels
      b. 1 level
      c. 5 levels
      d. 10000 levels

4. Adhya:paka
      a. teaches Ve:das
      b. imparts knowledge of sa:sthras
      c. lives in gurukulam
      d. teaches to talk

5. Guru
      a. dispels darkness on a topic
      b. means darkness
      c. lives in a:sram
      d. can fly

6. 'Ru' means
    a. one that adds
    b. one that disappears
    c. one that removes
    d. one that sticks

7. Second level knowledge
    a. deals with deeper understanding of elements
    b. talks about survival
    c. talks about creation
    d. talks about soul

8. A:cha:rya is similar to
    a. a great painter
    b. a great sculptor
    c. Sun
    d. a lotus

9. Whom does the famous Vedic phrase "A:cha:ryade:vo: Bhava" address?
    a. An a:cha:rya, of course!
    b. De:vatha:
    c. Me (a disciple)
    d. Both a:cha:rya and disciple

10. The following is greater than our physical birth
    a. Mental attitude
    b. Jna:na Janma by receiving knowledge from A:cha:rya
    c. Success in life
    d. Having a spiritual guru

11. Sa:stra means
    a. Science
    b. Social Studies
    c. Devotion
    d. Ve:das

12. A disciple in Sanskrit is called

    a.   sishya

    b.   bhagwa:n

    c.   sa:sthra

    d.   guru krupa

13. A:cha:ryade:vo: bhava means

    a.   worship A:cha:rya as De:vatha

    b.   worship Guru as A:cha:rya

    c.   worship A:cha:rya as God

    d.   None of the above

14. Gurukrupa

    a.   is the name of a Guru

    b.   means disciple

    c.   means grace of guru

    d.   none of the above

15. A:cha:rya bestows knowledge to make his disciples

    a.   rich

    b.   beautiful

    c.   useful citizens of the society

    d.   famous

II. Fill in the blanks

1. 'gu' means _____.

2. _____ teach the third level of knowledge.

3. Guru is _____ than the Sun.

4. Man uses _____ to perceive objects.

5. _____ teach the second level of knowledge.

6. Ve:das said 'a:cha:rya _____'.

7. The third level of knowledge deals with _____.

8. _____ provides us strong support and proper guidance.

9. a:chino:thi hi sa:sthra:rttha:n _____ sttha:payathyapi.

10. Our praiseworthy qualities are a reflection of our _____ greatness.

III. True or False

a. A:cha:rya is compared to a lamp.

b. Guru eradicates ignorance.

c. Moon makes the lotus flower blossom.

d. Parents give us knowledge.

e. A disciple's lifestyle should exhibit A:cha:rya's greatness.

IV. Match the following

a:cha:rya	removes ignorance
guru	worship a:cha:rya as God
adhya:paka	grace of guru
gurukrupa	teaches subjects in depth
a:cha:ryade:vo: bhava	teaches ultimate truth

V. One Word Answers

1. What is the purpose of the first level of knowledge?

   _____

2. What removes external darkness?

   _____

3. What removes inner darkness?

_____

4. Who removes the inner darkness?

_____

5. How many gurus can one have?

_____

VI. Answer the following

1. How can you get rid of ignorance?

_____

_____

2. Compare Sun to Guru.

_____

_____

3. Who is 'Adhya:paka'?

_____

_____

4. Compare A:cha:rya to a painter.

_____

_____

5. Compare A:cha:rya to a sculptor.

_____

_____

6. What kind of disciple does the world recognize?

    _____

    _____

7. Why is a:cha:rya important in one's life?

    _____

    _____

8. What do you learn from a lotus and the sun?

    _____

    _____

9. How can we be successful?

    _____

    _____

10. Explain the sloka *"a:chino:thi hi sa:sthra:rttha:n..."*

    _____

    _____

VII. Find the odd man out

a. guru, adhya:paka, a:cha:rya, teacher, parrot

b. Sun, lotus, water, rose, stone

c. painter, sculptor, writer, lamp, teacher

VIII. Analogy

a. sun = external darkness => guru = _____.

b. parents = physical life => guru = _____.

c. God's grace = sun => a:cha:rya's grace = _____.

d. a:cha:rya => disciple = _____ : painting

e. a:cha:rya = disciple => sculptor = _____.

IX. Fill in the slo:ka

a:chino:thi hi _____

_____ sttha:payathyapi

swayam _____ yasma:th

_____ _____ uchyathe:

X. Rearrange the words to form the sloka

1. 'gu'	2. sabdas	3. 'ru'
4. andhaka:ras	5. sabdasthu	6. ithy
7. abhidhi:yathe:	8. niro:dhathva:th	9. sya:th
10. thanniro:dhakaha	11. andhaka:ra	12. gurur

XI. Can you draw

a. A lotus blossoming under the sun light

b. Students learning in a classroom

c. A sculptor carving a stone

d. A milkman milking the cow

XII. Word Search

```
H  F  S  C  I  X  V  Z  T  Y  I  Y  S  E  P
A  C  C  U  R  A  T  E  V  I  E  C  R  E  P
W  A  R  O  U  N  I  V  E  R  S  A  L  U  N
Y  C  I  O  N  Q  I  Q  G  X  L  B  R  E  O
G  A  P  X  N  L  P  E  X  C  I  S  T  R  J
O  D  T  X  O  G  B  E  E  S  U  H  U  U  T
L  A  U  D  I  V  I  D  N  I  G  U  J  S  C
A  E  R  U  T  A  R  E  T  I  L  M  R  O  L
N  M  E  N  C  K  H  C  L  J  P  I  U  P  W
A  K  H  L  A  E  L  N  G  S  Q  L  B  X  M
V  C  L  D  R  R  E  A  C  Q  U  I  R  E  I
U  J  J  P  T  F  P  D  J  E  M  T  K  J  Y
M  W  M  U  S  E  S  I  J  W  D  Y  M  S  Z
N  O  I  T  I  S  I  U  Q  C  A  O  B  V  Q
C  A  V  F  D  O  D  G  F  O  H  W  Y  Q  H
```

ACCURATE	EXPOSURE
ACQUIRE	GUIDANCE
ACQUISITION	HUMILITY
ANALOGY	INDIVIDUAL
COMPREHENSIBLE	LITERATURE
DECLARE	PERCEIVE
DISPEL	PURSUIT
DISTRACTION	SCRIPTURE
ENLIGHTEN	UNIVERSAL

XIII.   Research

a.   Names of few scriptures

b.   Names of famous painters

c.   Names of great sculptors

d.   Instruments used by painters and sculptors

e.   Names of few gurus, adhya:paka:s, a:cha:ryas

XIV. Maze

Show him the way to gurukulam

XV. Do you remember?

1. What is Guru's Day? _____

2. When do we celebrate Guru's Day? _____

3. Whom do we pray on this day? _____

2. GURUDAKSHINA

I. Choose the correct answer

1. Dro:na's aim was to
   a. obtain capable disciples
   b. become rich
   c. become a great guru
   d. become guru to Arjuna

2. Dro:na blessed Arjuna
   a. to become the best archer in the world
   b. to have a long and victorious life
   c. because he showed his commitment
   d. because Arjuna was his favorite student

3. Dro:na's father was
   a. Sa:ndi:pani
   b. Duryo:dhana
   c. Sanjaya
   d. Angive:sa

4. Dro:na used grass blades as arrows by
   a. chanting a manthra
   b. using his powers
   c. using sticks and glue
   d. none of the above

5. _____ took up Dro:na's challenging task.
   a. Duryo:dhana
   b. Dharmara:ja
   c. Arjuna
   d. The Pa:ndavas and Kauravas

6. Drupada insulted Dro:**na**

    a. in gurukulum

    b. in Pa:ncha:la

    c. in a battle

    d. in Hasthina:pur

7. True disciples use their skills, prowess and strength

    a. to dominate everyone

    b. in service of their guru

    c. to earn money and fame

    d. to serve Nature and the community

8. If one insults a pious man, he will

    a. face defeat

    b. lead a prosperous life

    c. set a wrong example to all

    d. be loved by all

9. The moral of this story is

    a. Fulfill guru's wishes though they are challenging

    b. Always be humble before your a:cha:rya

    c. Always become an instrument for your guru

    d. All of the above

10. A real disciple is _____

    a. humble, devoted, rich, headstrong

    b. committed, humble, obedient

    c. humble, devoted, arrogant, egotistic

    d. He who feels he knows everything

II. Fill in the blanks

1. _____ and _____ were playing Kara.

2. Dro:na was an expert in _____.

3. A token of gratitude given to an a:cha:rya is called _____

4. Dro:na was very pleased with Arjuna's _____.

5. Arjuna captured _____.

III. True or False

1. Bhi:ma appointed Dro:na as guru to Kauravas only.

2. Dro:na taught fishing.

3. Drupada and Bhi:shma were friends once upon a time.

4. Drupada insulted Dro:na.

5. Dro:na wanted the kingdom as gurudakshina.

6. Kauravas were not able to give gurudakshina.

7. Dharmara:ja felt unhappy when Kauravas were defeated.

8. Arjuna was able to defeat Drupada.

9. Dhruthara:shtra blessed Arjuna to become the best archer in the world.

10. A guru demands gurudakshina as fees from a student.

IV. How are they related to Arjuna

1. Bhi:shma:cha:rya   a) uncle
2. Dhruthara:shtra   b) guru's enemy
3. Drupada   c) wife
4. Drona:cha:rya   d) father
5. Kauravas   e) brother-in-law
6. Dharmara:ja   f) cousins
7. Agnive:sa   g) guru
8. Gauthama   h) guru's father
9. Nakula   i) great grandfather
10. Sahade:va   j) elder brother
11. Bhi:ma   k) guru's friend
12. Draupadi   l) younger brother
13. Kunthi   m) mother
14. Pa:ndu
15. Krushna

V. Who said to Whom

1. "A:cha:rya! With your grace, we have completed the course. What can we offer you?"

   _____

2. "Your kingly qualities are very poor. Your education in weaponry is incomplete."

   _____

3. "I don't need wealth or land"

   _____

4. "A:cha:rya! We have brought you King Drupada as per your command."

   _____

VI. Correct the Spellings

Panchala

Dronacharya

Acharya

Bramhana

Bhima

Dharmaraja

Sahadeva

Gurdakina

VII. Short Answer

1. Who was Dro:**n**a's classmate.

   _____

2. Who was Duryo:dhana's father?

   _____

3. Who was the teacher of Pa:ndavas and Kauravas?

   _____

4. Which game is similar to the game Kara?

   _____

5. Who brought the ball and ring out of the well?

   _____

6. Who defeated Drupada?

   _____

7. Where did Drupada and Dro:**n**a:cha:rya study?

   _____

8. What did Dro:na expect from Drupada?

_____

9. Who was the king of Hasthina:pura?

_____

10. Who were the princes of Hasthina:pura?

_____

VIII. Answer the following

1. What is gurudakshina?

_____

_____

2. Why and when is gurudakshina given?

_____

_____

3. How did Arjuna offer gurudakshina to Dro:na? What do we learn from this?

_____

_____

4. What did Dro:na:cha:rya want as gurudakshina? Why?

_____

_____

5. How did Arjuna become a world renowned archer?

_____

_____

IX. Rearrange the sentences in order

1. Drupada and Dro:na studied together. ____

2. Arjuna proved his respect and devotion towards his A:cha:rya. ___

3. Dhruthara:shtra was ruling Hasthina:pur. ____

4. Arjuna offered gurudakshina. ____

5. Dro:na taught the princes of Hasthina:pur. ____

6. Dro:na asked his disciples to capture Drupada and bring him as Gurudakshina. ____

7. Drupada insulted Dro:na. ____

8. Drupada promised to help Dro:na when required. ____

X. Find the 15 differences between, the two pictures

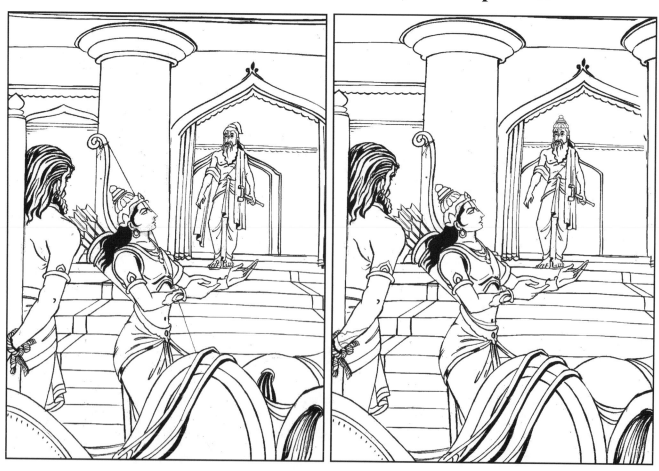

XI. Who am I?

1. The kids threw me into the well. Someone used grass blades and pulled me out of the well. Thank God! I thought I would be stuck in there forever. Who am I?

2. I promised my guru that I would do anything for him. I made my guru happy! Who am I?

3. A king forgot about the values of friendship. He insulted his childhood friend. Unfortunately, he rules me. Who am I?

4. The great grandfather of Kauravas and Pa:ndavas took care of me. He was my keeper and protected me. Who am I?

5. I appointed a great archer Dro:na:cha:rya as a teacher to the princes. Who am I?

6. Pa:ndava:s captured Drupada and tied him to me. I brought him to Drona:cha:rya. Who am I?

7. We went to capture Drupada but he overpowered us. Who are we?

8. Drupada defeated my cousins. Then, my brothers and I went to fight against Drupada. Who am I?

XII. **What are the qualities a disciple must possess? Offer them as flowers while doing puja to a:cha:rya. Color the picture.**

XIII. Let Us Learn

a) Guru is like a cloud. How?

Dark blue clouds shower pure water without any constraints. After giving us all the cool, sweet and potable water, the clouds still feel that they did not give anything and become pale.

Similarly, a:cha:rya, out of compassion, blesses the disciples with knowledge. Nevertheless, He feels dissatisfied that he did not do anything and yearns to give more knowledge. Thus a:cha:rya, with his magnanimity, always gives good messages.

Being good disciples, we always need to be attentive in grasping those messages.

b) What are the differences between storm and cumulus clouds?

b) A student should be like a crow. How?

Among all birds, the crow is known to be very energetic and has a helping nature. Scriptures suggest that a student should be active like a crow.

XIV. Time Travel

Imagine that you were one of the students of Dro:**na**. Describe your guru's happiness when Pa:ndavas captured Drupada.

XV. Can you draw?

1. The princes learning warfare

2. Dro:**na** hugging Arjuna

3. Battle field

4. Arjuna tossing captured Drupada at the feet of his guru Dro:**na**

XVI. Word Search

```
A   M   W   Y   V   S   V   E   K   N   V   C   Z   X   N
T   E   B   Y   Z   G   U   S   A   N   C   T   I   T   Y
V   P   X   M   D   P   R   O   W   E   S   S   Y   O   R
U   R   C   N   E   W   U   J   I   C   E   E   M   E   S
A   I   W   C   N   F   T   C   G   R   I   N   C   S   K
T   N   E   M   N   G   I   S   S   A   O   I   W   E   I
U   C   H   C   U   G   U   E   Z   I   P   T   V   L   L
F   E   S   I   H   Y   C   U   T   R   Q   O   C   P   L
S   S   P   T   S   A   W   O   O   C   K   G   F   I   S
E   L   U   R   R   A   V   C   K   E   D   P   G   C   V
E   C   A   B   R   E   A   G   V   R   E   K   Q   S   R
D   X   M   F   D   T   Y   R   E   H   C   R   A   I   D
K   E   A   N   E   H   U   F   W   B   F   E   O   D   N
J   R   D   O   C   G   A   S   N   P   H   E   P   D   S
E   E   B   S   K   W   R   B   E   Q   R   L   U   K   L
```

ARCHERY	RECIPROCATE
ASSIGNMENT	RULE
DEVOTION	SANCTITY
DISCIPLES	SHUNNED
EMBRACE	SKILLS
EVOKE	VICTORIOUS
PRINCES	WARFARE
PROWESS	

XVII. Double Puzzle. Unscramble each of the clue words. Copy the letters in the numbered cells to other cells with the same number to solve the puzzle.

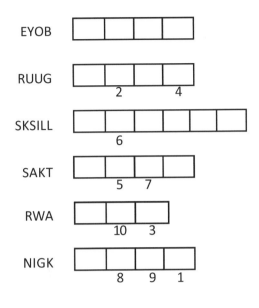

EYOB

RUUG   2   4

SKSILL   6

SAKT   5   7

RWA   10   3

NIGK   8   9   1

1   2   3   4   D   H   5   6   7   8   9   10

XVIII. Do you Remember?

1. Which manthra should one chant before starting any work?

   _____

2. Who is your first teacher?

   _____

3. What do you learn from pet animals?

   _____

4. What do friends teach us?

   _____

5. What do neighbors teach us?

   _____

XIX. Complete the family tree. Can you expand it further?

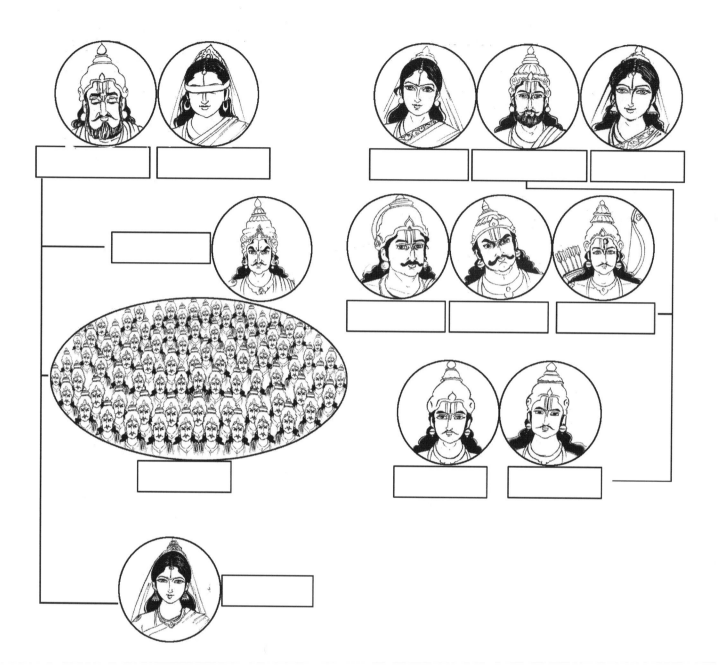

XX. Maze

Arjuna is taking Drupada tied to chariot to offer him as gurudakshiṇa at his guru's lotus feet. Can you help him find the way back to Hasthina:pur?

XXI. Research

Compare and contrast the education today with the education provided a few hundreds of years ago.

XXII. Let us practice – Serve All Beings as Service to God

A country's strength is its citizens. If the citizens are good, honest and have integrity, the country will progress. Today's children are tomorrow's citizens.

To become a good citizen, you must learn and practice good things. You must do well in school, participate in extra-curricular activities, perform community service, and also participate in arts, sports, dance, music, etc. This will help to improve your personality and make you a good citizen, which will in turn help in the development of the country. VT Seva is planning to conduct a personality development camp. You are incharge of sports. What sports would you plan to have during this camp?

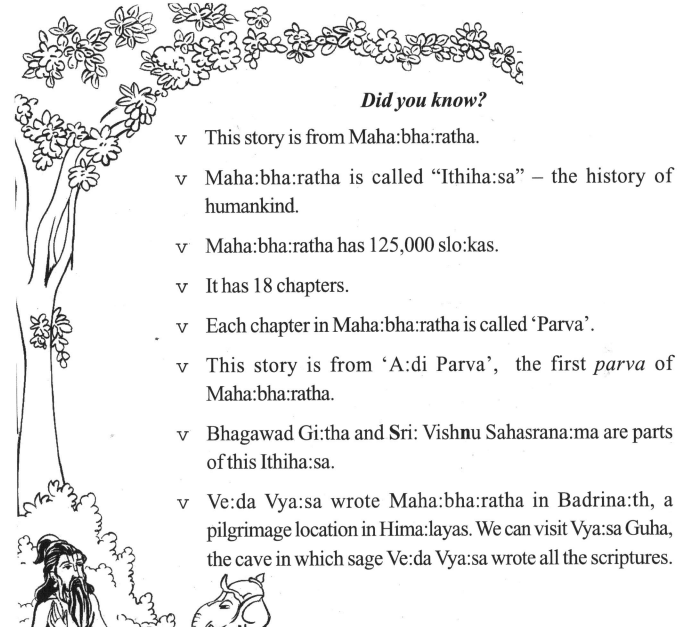

Did you know?

v   This story is from Maha:bha:ratha.

v   Maha:bha:ratha is called "Ithiha:sa" – the history of humankind.

v   Maha:bha:ratha has 125,000 slo:kas.

v   It has 18 chapters.

v   Each chapter in Maha:bha:ratha is called 'Parva'.

v   This story is from 'A:di Parva', the first *parva* of Maha:bha:ratha.

v   Bhagawad Gi:tha and Sri: Vishnu Sahasrana:ma are parts of this Ithiha:sa.

v   Ve:da Vya:sa wrote Maha:bha:ratha in Badrina:th, a pilgrimage location in Hima:layas. We can visit Vya:sa Guha, the cave in which sage Ve:da Vya:sa wrote all the scriptures.

Words of Wisdom

Always have gratitude towards your teacher. Remember to offer gurudakshina to your guru. Gurudakshina can be in any form that pleases the guru.

3. SECRET OF SUCCESS

I. Choose the correct answer

1. In olden days, disciples

   a. read using computers

   b. read only one lesson per day

   c. ate fruits only

   d. did madhu:karam

2. Upamanyu became blind because

   a. he read books under moonlight

   b. guru cursed him

   c. poisonous sap fell in his eyes

   d. none of the above

3. Dhaumya Maharshi had

   a. cattle

   b. a lot of money

   c. a kingdom

   d. no money at all

4. Gurus tested students

   a. once in a year

   b. to check their zeal to learn

   c. to charge fees accordingly

   d. for name sake

5. 'Madhu:karam' means

   a. collecting honey

   b. removing obstacles

   c. a reward to a:cha:rya

   d. begging alms

6. Guruji _____ Upamanyu.

    a. punished

    b. tested

    c. hated

    d. neglected

7. Upamanyu ate _____ in the forest.

    a. roots

    b. bubbles

    c. leaves and fruits

    d. rice

8. Guruji went to forest

    a. in search of Upamanyu

    b. in search of the cows

    c. to meet the Aswini De:vathas

    d. to bring wood

9. Upamanyu accepted his teacher's words as a

    a. prayer

    b. command

    c. request

    d. suggestion

10. Upamanyu earned a place in history because

    a. he conquered hunger

    b. he learned the Holy Ve:das

    c. of his unsurpassed devotion and love towards his guru

    d. Aswini de:vathas blessed him

11. Choose the correct statements

    a. All students were treated equally

    b. The mentors were very sincere

    c. Mentors were responsible protectors of Dharma

    d. Mentors were interested in making money

12. Students had to do Madhu:karam to

    a. earn money

    b. get rid of ego and false prestige

    c. become famous

    d. none of the above

13. Upamanyu went to forest everyday

    a. to meditate

    b. to cut firewood

    c. to graze cattle

    d. to do madhu:karam

14. Gurus

    a. imparted knowledge to students

    b. moulded students into good citizens

    c. taught discipline to students

    d. all of the above

15. Upamanyu accepted his guru's command

    a. with great difficulty

    b. forcefully

    c. obediently

    d. none of the above

II. Fill in the blanks

1. Sage Dhaumya was eager to test _____ of his disciple.

2. _____ were responsible protectors of righteousness.

3. Upamanyu had great faith and _____ towards his guru.

4. Students served their _____ loyally.

5. Upamanyu wanted only the grace of his _____ .

III. True or False

1. Gurus did not charge fees to impart education.

2. The calves stopped drinking milk because of Upamanyu's deeds.

3. Guruji gave delicious food to Upamanyu everyday.

4. Guru blessed Bramha Vidya to Upamanyu.

5. Upamanyu lost his eyesight as he didn't obey his a:cha:rya.

6. The story of Upamanyu is an example of Pithru De:vo:bhava.

7. Upamanyu always had faith in his guru.

8. Agni de:vatha blessed Upamanyu with eyesight.

9. Sage Dhaumya's wife prevented him from going to forest.

10. Upamanyu was angry with his Guru.

IV. Match the Definitions

1. a:cha:rya se:va   a) service to a:cha:rya

2. madhu:karam   b) ultimate knowledge

3. bramha vidya   c) an act of collecting alms from different homes and offering to guru

4. Aswini De:vathas   d) an act of righteousness

5. dharma   e) doctors of de:vathas called Mithra and Varuna

V. Who said to Whom

1. 'Do not deprive the calves of their mother's milk'

   _____

2. 'I am only drinking the froth dripping from the calves' mouth'

   _____

3. 'I will accept help with the blessings of my A:cha:rya only'

_____

4. 'We can cure your blindness and you will be able to see again'

_____

VI. Rearrange the sentences in order

a. The calves might stop drinking more milk. _____

b. Upamanyu stayed in Sage Dhaumya's gurukulam. _____

c. Guruji, I am eating the leaves and fruits. _____

d. All the cows except Upamanyu reached the a:sram. _____

e. The cows might stop feeding their calves. _____

f. Upamanyu got his eyesight back. _____

g. Dhaumya blessed Upamanyu with 'Bramha Vidya' _____

h. Upamanyu took the cows to the forest everyday. _____

i. Aswini De:vathas did not know what to do. _____

j. Guru took away all the food from Upamanyu. _____

k. Guru decided to test Upamanyu. _____

VII. Correct the spellings

1. Madhukaram

2. Upmanyu:

3. Dhama

4. Brahmaviddyaa

5. Ashwini Devetaas

VIII. One Word Answers

1. Who was Upamanyu's guru?

   _____

2. Who restored eyesight to Upamanyu?

   _____

3. Who sent Guruji to the forest?

   _____

4. Where was Upamanyu found?

   _____

5. What did Upamanyu get ultimately?

   _____

IX. Answer the following

1. Describe the education procedure in olden days.

   _____

   _____

2. What is 'Madhu:karam'? Why did students do Madhu:karam?

   _____

   _____

3. Did Guruji like Upamanyu? Explain.

   _____

   _____

4. Describe guru bhakthi of Upamanyu.

   _____

   _____

5. What is the moral of the story?

   _____

   _____

X. Who am I?

1. I took away the eyesight of a young boy. Who am I?

2. We went to forest everyday to eat. However, our master did not eat regular food. Who are we?

3. My guru blessed me after a long trial. Who am I?

4. We are very divine and donot touch the ground. We are specialists in Medicine. Who are we?

5. Suddenly a blind, hungry boy fell in me. Who am I?

6. I forced my husband to look for Upamanyu. Who am I?

7. All these years, neither birds nor animals were eating us. Suddenly this boy started eating us. We wonder how we tasted! Who are we?

XI. Comprehension - Perseverance

Ashta:kshari: manthra is regarded as the greatest of all the manthras. Only a few a:cha:ryas knew the manthra and meditated on it. They guarded this manthra closely. A:cha:ryas put their students through rigorous exams to test their faith and interest in the knowledge before giving them the manthra.

Our great guru, Sri: Ra:ma:nuja:cha:rya wanted to know the meaning of a manthra called charama slo:ka. He approached Sri: Go:shtti:pu:rna to learn it. However, Sri Go:shtti:pu:rna turned down his request seventeen times. Undeterred, Sri: Ra:ma:nuja:cha:rya trekked hundreds of miles on foot and approached the guru time and again. Finally the 18th time, guru was satisfied with Sri: Ra:ma:nuja:cha:rya's resolute determination and revealed the secrets of charama slo:ka. Sri: Ra:ma:nuja:cha:rya was thrilled to finally learn the meaning of the manthra.

Sri: Ra:ma:nuja:cha:rya, being a renowned monk of his day, did not hesitate to go to a guru to get the meaning of the manthra. He also bore the pain of walking hundreds of miles repeatedly to reach the place where Sri: Go:shtti:pu:rna lived. He did not feel shy to approach a:cha:rya time and again to get initiated and gain higher knowledge. He revered the rule of the scriptures that manthra and its meaning should be acquired from a guru.

True or False

1. Ra:ma:nuja:cha:rya approached Sri: Rangana:ttha to learn the manthra.

2. Gurus test the interest and faith of the disciple.

3. Guruji revealed the meaning of the manthra in the first visit itself.

4. Ra:ma:nuja:cha:rya had reverence towards scriptures.

5. Go:shtti:pu:rna was the disciple of Ra:ma:nuja:cha:rya.

Questions

1. What qualities do you observe in **Sri:** Ra:ma:nuja as a disciple?

   _____

   _____

2. Who is the guru of **Sri:** Ra:ma:nuja?

   _____

   _____

3. How did Ra:ma:nuja's guru test him?

   _____

   _____

4. Would you approach your guru to learn something 18 times?

   _____

   _____

XII. How many Sanskrit or English words can you make using letters from 'MADHU:KARAM'.

XIII. Time Travel

Imagine you are a student of a gurukulam about 500 years ago.
Write a paragraph on how you would spend your day.

XIV. Spot at least 10 differences

XV. Let Us Learn

Guru is like a bird. Learn how. Birds fly. To fly across the skies, birds use their two wings.

In the same way, a:cha:rya uses KNOWLEDGE and PRACTICE as his wings. Sky is called A:ka:**sa** in Sanskrit. Birds fly in a:ka:**sa**. So also, gurus. Here a:ka:**sa** does not mean the open sky.

* A: + ka:**sa** becomes A:ka:**sa**.

* A: = all over

* ka:**sa** = that shines

A:ka:sa means God who shines all over as omnipresent. A:cha:ryas not only realize the omnipresence of God, but also serve Him in all respects. Thus a:cha:ryas are compared to birds that fly in a:ka:sa.

What can a student learn from a dog?

A dog has control over its sleep. It has the ability to remain alert even during the sleep. It never thinks, "I slept for less time or someone disturbed my sleep." Similarly, a student should be alert in receiving knowledge whenever it is available as well and have control over his sleep.

a. Draw the picture of a student who is sleeping. How can you show that he is sleeping alertly?

b. Draw other creatures which are alert during sleep.

XV. Word Search

```
D  N  L  K  Y  C  O  Z  G  S  V  N  W  C  M
I  E  R  E  Z  W  X  B  E  U  K  K  O  V  A
R  E  S  G  A  E  D  R  E  E  M  N  D  C  S
D  T  S  S  R  R  O  C  A  D  D  E  L  Q  T
F  N  R  H  A  H  N  G  C  U  I  N  H  V  E
Y  S  A  Q  C  P  E  F  C  N  O  E  P  R  R
G  U  L  M  D  R  R  T  S  I  Q  Q  N  H  E
Q  O  O  J  M  N  V  U  T  P  T  P  Z  T  D
F  E  H  Y  D  O  H  U  S  R  O  T  N  E  M
X  G  C  L  D  A  C  U  S  N  U  Y  T  Y  E
B  A  S  U  Y  E  G  W  N  O  U  A  Q  L  C
F  R  A  E  X  H  M  D  H  A  R  M  A  O  X
P  U  T  E  G  R  O  O  Y  M  Q  D  C  Y  L
V  O  A  U  T  H  O  R  I  T  Y  Z  E  A  S
V  C  T  T  I  H  T  X  R  T  U  P  L  L  K
```

AUTHORITY	DHARMA	MASTERED
CHORES	EAGER	MENTORS
COMMAND	EXECUTION	OBEDIENT
CONDUCT	LEARN	SCHOLAR
COURAGEOUS	LOYAL	UNSURPASSED

XVI. Sort the duties and qualities of a guru and a disciple from the word bank below and note them in the appropriate posters

1. Use knowledge properly

2. A:cha:rya se:va

3. Discipline

4. Honesty

5. Integrity

6. Guidance

7. Good communication

8. Madhu:karam

9. Determination to learn

10. Serve loyally

11. Learn eagerly

12. Test aptitude

13. Good conduct

14. Remove ego

15. Unquestionably execute tasks assigned

16. Give equal treatment to rich or poor

17. Never question the instructions

18. Commitment

19. Full authority to instruct

20. Mould into good and brave citizens

21. Determined to safeguard dharma

22. Pass various tests successfully

23. Perseverance

24. Devotion

25. Faith

26. Obey

27. Love

Guru

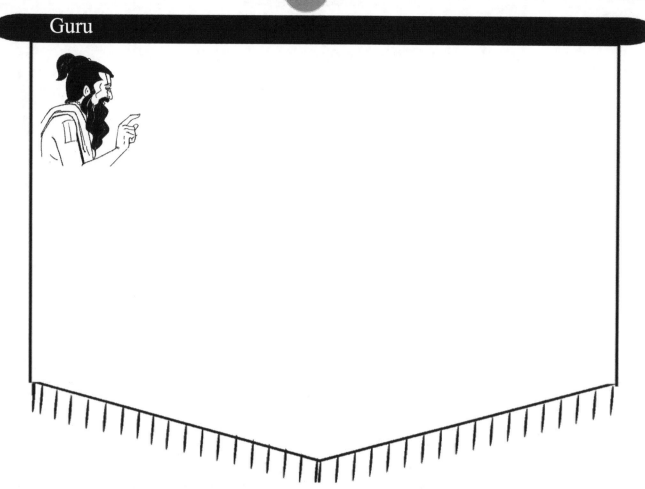

Sishya

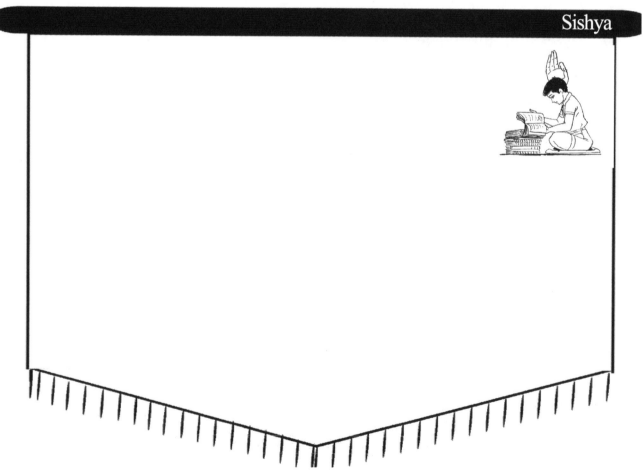

XVII. **Sage Dhaumya is trying to reach Upamanyu. Can you help him?**

XVIII. **Illustrate the following**

1. Dhaumya instructing Upamanyu to take care of the cows.

2. Upamanyu drinking milk from the cows.

3. Guruji's wife asking Guru to search for Upamanyu.

XIX. Do you remember?

1. How do you respect a guru?

    _____

2. How do you prostrate before a guru?

    _____

XX. Let us practice – Serve all beings as service to God

Upamanyu became blind. Aswini de:vathas helped him to become a normal kid again. We too can help in such causes. VT Seva is conducting a walk-a-thon on Jan 4th to create awareness about blindness.

A. You are part of the VT Seva walk-a-thon publicity team. Create a poster for this event.

B. You are planning to participate in the walkathon raising $500 to support a visually challenged student from VT Seva Nethra Vidyalaya. How and what will you do to raise funds for your 10 K walk? Write at least 5 different ways of collecting funds to reach your target.

XXI. Research

1. Name the disciples who followed guru's instructions.

2. Details of Aswini de:vathas.

3. Names of a few poisonous plants.

4. Ithiha:sas and their names.

5. Compare your classroom with a classroom in gurukulam. List atleast 5 differences.

6. Find out the class timings in a gurukulam.

7. Compare the existing facilities you have with the same the students had 500 years ago.

XXII. Conclusions and Food for Thought

* What is the biggest obstacle that stops one from learning further? How did the old system curb this quality from growing in the disciples? (**Hint:** "vidya: dada:thi vinayam")

* The more one learns, the more humble one should become. If not, that knowledge is dangerous! Upamanyu, inspite of the hard tests, never doubted the integrity of his Guru. Even de:vathas came to help him. The one who has complete trust in his A:cha:rya never fails in reaching the ultimate goal.

Words of Wisdom
Never question the instructions of a:cha:rya.
Have unsurpassed love and devotion towards a:cha:rya.

Did you know?

This story is from 3rd Chapter of A:di Parva. A:di parva is from Maha:bha:ratha.

Upamanyu was the younger brother and a disciple of Sage Dhaumya. Dhaumya was also called Apo:da Dhaumya or A:po:da Dhaumya or A:yo:dha Dhaumya.

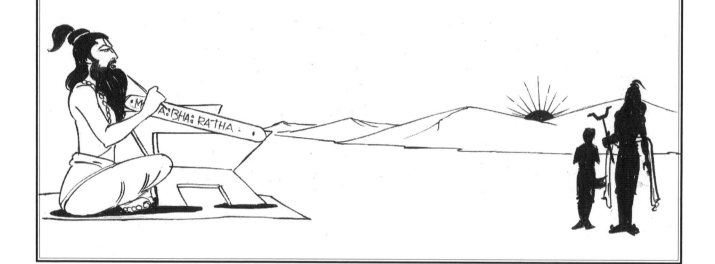

4. CARE FOR A:CHA:RYA BY ALL MEANS

I. Choose the correct answer

1. Sri:rangam is
   - a. name of a boy
   - b. first temple on earth
   - c. name of a book
   - d. a train

2. Ra:ma:nuja:cha:rya
   - a. used to visit Sri: Rangana:ttha everyday
   - b. was a priest at Sri:rangam
   - c. didn't take thi:rttham one day
   - d. built a palace

3. After various attempts on life, Ra:ma:nuja:cha:rya survived
   - a. by drinking Ka:ve:ri water
   - b. by cooking food Himself
   - c. by doing bhiksha
   - d. none of the above

4. The holy water offered in temple is called
   - a. satta:ri
   - b. prasa:dam
   - c. thi:rttham
   - d. phalam

5. While prostrating to elders
   - a. we should not cry
   - b. we should not get up till they say so
   - c. we should not close our eyes
   - d. we should do it in front of everyone

6. The priest's wife

    a. mixed poison in the food

    b. wanted to warn Ra:ma:nuja:cha:rya about poisonous food

    c. was a disciple of Vaduganambi

    d. went to Lord Rangana:ttha's temple

7. Ra:ma:nuja:cha:rya's guruji was

    a. A:ndhrapu:rna

    b. Go:shtti:pu:rna

    c. Sri: Rangana:ttha

    d. Vaduganambi

8. Vaduganambi's devotion towards A:cha:rya was

    a. proved by his words

    b. recognized by Go:shttipurna

    c. tested by the disciples

    d. not pure

9. Surrender means

    a. being timid

    b. prostrating

    c. you and I are same

    d. unconditional submission

10. The poisoned food

    a. was eaten by a dog and crow

    b. distributed to all

    c. was eaten by a cat

    d. none of the above

II. Fill in the blanks

1. The main deity in Sri:rangam is _____.

2. Ra:ma:nuja:cha:rya was an ardent devotee of _____.

3. While offering food, do not have _____ in your eyes.

4. Before prostrating to guru, Ra:ma:nuja:cha:rya removed his _____.

5. One of the disciples could not tolerate the passive attitude of _____.

6. Ra:ma:nuja:cha:rya's disciple placed Ra:ma:nuja:cha:rya's body on his _____.

7. Vadugambi had great _____ and dedication towards Ra:ma:nuja:cha:rya.

8. _____ gave permission to cook food for Ra:ma:nuja:cha:rya.

9. There is no one equal to Vaduganambi in _____.

10. Vaduganambi was also called _____.

III. True or False

1. Ra:ma:nuja:cha:rya's disciple was very angry with Go:shtti:pu:rna.

2. Ra:ma:nuja:cha:rya constructed the Sri:rangam temple.

3. Priest's wife did not want to give bhiksha to Ra:ma:nuja:cha:rya.

4. One should not touch the recipient's feet while giving bhiksha.

5. The priests used to respect Ra:ma:nuja:cha:rya a lot.

IV. Match the following

1. A:ndhrapu:rna   a. guru
2. Ra:ma:nuja:cha:rya   b. took care of guru's welfare
3. Go:shtti:pu:rna   c. took care of Lord Rangana:ttha
4. priest   d. victim of poison
5. crow   e. poisoned food

V. Match the Definitions

1. thi:rttham   a. wooden sandals
2. bhiksha   b. ultimate message given by Krushna to mankind
3. charama slo:ka   c. food given by house owners to a monk
4. pa:duka:s   d. holy water

VI. Who said to Whom?

1. 'You can resume your regular activities.'

   _____

2. 'Nothing will harm my guru now!'

   _____

3. 'Now do as you wish.'

   _____

VII. Rearrange the sentences in order

1. Ra:ma:nuja:cha:rya did sa:shta:ngam to Go:shtti:pu:rna._____
2. Priests did not like Ra:ma:nuja:cha:rya. _____
3. Go:shtti:pu:rna wanted to meet Ra:ma:nuja:cha:rya. _____
4. They mixed poison in thi:rttham and food. _____
5. Ra:ma:nuja:cha:rya's disciple was unable to tolerate the sufferings of his guru. _____

6. Ra:ma:nuja:cha:rya stopped taking bhiksha. _____

7. It was hot summer. _____

8. He laid down immediately and placed Ra:ma:nuja:cha:rya on his back. _____

9. Guruji did not ask Ra:ma:nuja:cha:rya to get up. _____

10. Ra:ma:nuja:cha:rya's body was turning red because of the hot sand. _____

VIII. Correct the Spellings

1. Bhi:ksha:

2. Ra:ma:nja:char:ya

3. Ghostiparna

4. Vadumanambi

5. SrRangam

6. Lord Ranganutha

7. Prostate

8. Kuvuri

9. Pudakas

10. AndhraPuri

IX. One Word Answers

1. Where did Ra:ma:nuja:cha:rya spend most of his time?

   _____

2. Which temple did Ra:ma:nuja:cha:rya try to regularize?

   _____

3. What did Ra:ma:nuja:cha:rya take in the temple everyday?

_____

4. How many homes did the monks visit for bhiksha?

_____

5. How many gurus did Ra:ma:nuja:cha:rya have?

_____

6. What did Ra:ma:nuja:cha:rya learn from Go:shtti:pu:rna?

_____

7. Where did Ra:ma:nuja:cha:rya meet Go:shtti:pu:rna?

_____

8. Who was Ra:ma:nuja:cha:rya's chef?

_____

9. Where did Go:shtti:pu:rna live?

_____

10. Who saved Ra:ma:nuja:cha:rya from the poisoned food?

_____

X. Answer the following

1. Explain the glory of Sri: Rangana:ttha.

_____

_____

2. Why were the temple priests angry?

_____

_____

3. Why were the temple priests disappointed?

_____

_____

4. Who was Go:shtti:pu:rna? How did he help Ra:ma:nuja:cha:rya?

   _____

   _____

5. Explain the devotion of Vaduganambi.

   _____

   _____

6. Why did Ra:ma:nuja:cha:rya stop taking bhiksha?

   _____

   _____

XI. Who am I?

1. Ra:ma:nuja:cha:rya carried me in His hands. Even Chinna Jeeyar Swa:miji carries me all the time. What am I? _____

2. I am made of wood. Saints use me. If I am not worn by my owner and placed somewhere, people worship me and put me on their heads for blessings. Who am I? _____

3. I served poisonous food to a monk by force but warned him. Who am I? _____

4. I am all-pervasive and all-powerful. I appeared on this Earth in deity form on banks of River Ka:ve:ri. Who am I? _____

5. I revealed the meaning of charama slo:ka to Ra:ma:nuja:cha:rya the 18th time he approached me. Who am I? _____

XII. How many words can you make using the word "Lord Rangana:ttha"

XIII. Let Us Learn

Guru is like an ocean. How?

Analogy - 1

Many rivers flow into an ocean. But the ocean never changes its form or shape. Similarly, a:cha:rya doesn't loose his practices and effulgence inspite of being in the midst of society and moving around with people having different practices.

Draw various rivers of India joining in Bay of Bengal and color the picture.

gy - 2

An ocean is full of wealth. Similarly, a:cha:rya possesses vast amount of knowledge. Draw ocean an
show different kinds of wealth found in the ocean. Color the picture.

Analogy - 3

A few dive into the ocean to get pearls and precious stones. A few catch fish for their livelihood. A few drill the ocean bed to get natural gases. Some just dive in to enjoy the beauty of the ocean. In the same way, different people approach a:cha:rya for different purposes. Few disciples approach a:cha:rya to gain knowledge. Others approach a:cha:rya to have his darshan and enjoy his divine presence. A few come to seek his advice while others approach him for materialistic things. It is up to individual disciples on how they choose to get a:cha:rya's blessings.

Q) Why would you approach a:cha:rya? Explain.

Student should be like a crane. How?

A crane stands for hours together in complete concentration without moving, until it gets the prey. After eating its fill, it again stands in the same way to catch small fish for its young ones. Similarly a student should have focus and patience until he gets the required knowledge.

XIV. In the picture below Vaduganambi is boiling milk and Kidambi A:chcha:n is cooking prasa:dar for Ra:ma:nuja. Color this picture.

XV. Time Travel

Imagine you were a disciple of Bhagavad Ra:ma:nuja:cha:rya living in 1100 AD. How would you react if someone was about to hurt your guru?

XVI. Spot atleast 10 differences

XVII. Comprehension

At the beginning of creation, Lord Vishnu brings the universe out from within Him. At the time of dissolution, he swallows and preserves the entire universe inside Him. Thus, the universe is always under His control. To support the universe, He takes several incarnations called avatha:ras to eliminate evil and to protect righteousness.

Every year, He deeply meditates for four months. This meditation is called 'Yo:ganidra'. 'Yo:ga' means union and 'Nidra' means coming back from regular activity. During Yo:ganidra, He focuses on finding new ways to protect the Universe. During this period, He identifies several people to implement His plan. Those chosen few become our Gurus. The Lord starts this process of Yo:ganidra on A:sha:**dha** Pu:rnima. Hence, this day is set to honor our gurus. This is one of the reasons why we call this day as Guru Pu:rnima

One cha:thurma:syam, Lord decided to send A:dise:sha as a:cha:rya Bhagawad Ra:ma:nujacha:rya to guide people and show them the path to get ultimate bliss. Thus Bhagawad Ra:ma:nuja:cha:rya appeared on this earth 1000 years ago. Ra:ma:nuja:cha:rya went against the rigid society practices and gave the ashta:kshari: manthra to all, irrespective of their caste or creed. His efforts to uplift everyone from this mundane world were immeasurable.

True or False

1. God sleeps for four months.
2. Garuda appeared on earth as Bhagawad Ra:ma:nuja:cha:rya.
3. God takes incarnations to protect righteousness.
4. Lord starts his meditation on **Sra:va**na Pu:rnima.
5. God gave manthra to a few selected people.
6. A:sha:**dha** Pu:rnima is also called Guru Pu:rnima.
7. The four months of Lord's meditation is called 'Yo:ga Nidra'.
8. The four months are very sa:thvic and one should do good activities.

XVIII. Let us practice – Serve All Beings as Service to God

Man needs food, clothing and shelter to survive. However, a few under privileged are deprived of these minimum requirements. It is our duty to do some service to them.

Every Sunday, VT Seva hands over 200 burritos, juice, milk and candies to the Shelter Home. Every week, 15 volunteers gather at a place to make the burritos. This year, you have been appointed as the new Food Coordinator. List the different responsibilities you have to perform to make sure that 200 people get their lunches on time.

XIX. Word Search

```
C  E  T  A  R  T  S  O  R  P  A  D  D  R  P
V  O  J  V  K  Y  H  L  V  A  E  I  E  W  O
N  E  N  D  E  N  W  S  H  E  H  C  D  H  N
Q  O  E  S  R  S  Y  J  C  I  I  Q  I  E  D
O  C  I  G  P  T  T  O  W  P  H  M  C  V  E
N  U  Z  T  L  I  R  E  I  J  N  K  A  X  R
F  O  O  S  O  P  R  E  D  I  W  E  T  R  C
P  V  F  G  K  V  N  A  B  V  V  L  I  Q  D
A  X  K  A  S  T  E  T  C  Q  B  R  O  P  E
F  Z  J  H  Y  A  O  D  H  Y  S  M  N  B  Y
E  T  N  S  T  E  M  P  L  E  I  D  V  Q  Z
M  J  V  K  N  T  Y  D  P  V  G  S  O  X  B
H  D  R  I  R  A  P  T  N  O  R  J  E  M  R
K  H  S  H  N  N  E  L  K  S  I  G  P  U  J
G  H  Q  B  E  Y  B  E  I  T  H  W  O  I  V
```

BHIKSHA	PROCEED
CONSPIRACY	PROSTRATE
DEDICATION	RECIPIENT
DEVOTION	TEMPLE
PONDER	VESTED

XX. Here is the picture of a:lwa:rs and lineage of A:cha:ryas. Research and find names.

XXI. **Go:shtti:pu:rna is trying to reach Ra:ma:nuja:cha:rya. Can you help him?**

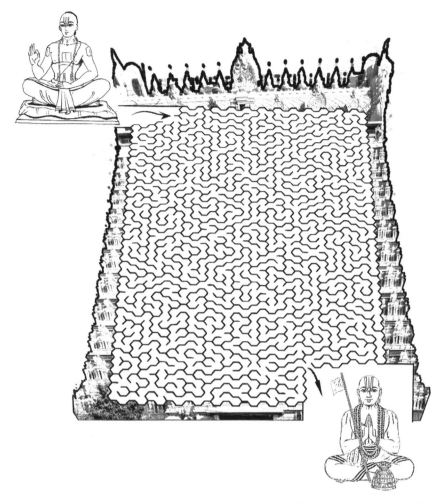

XXII. **Unscramble each of the clue words. Copy the letters in the numbered cells to the cells below with the same number to solve the puzzle.**

HOYL

2

DOLR

RUEL

MKNO

3

NAKB

1   4

		I		S		
1	2	3		2	4	

XXIII. Do you remember?

You read this guru pra:rtthana in Module 1.

gurur bramha: gurur vishnuhu
gurur de:vo: mahe:swaraha|
gurus sa:ksha:th para bramha
thasmai sri: gurave: namaha||

1. To whom are you offering salutations in the above slo:ka? Why?
2. Anyone who cultivates good thinking or creates new objects becomes
_____, in a limited way.
3. Anyone who puts their thinking or objects in use becomes
_____, in a limited way.
4. Anyone who removes ignorance or destroys objects becomes
_____.

XXIV. Research

1. What is the dresscode of a student in gurukulam?

2. In which countries do we find gurukulams?

3. How is your teacher different from the guru in gurukulam? List atleast 5 differences.

Words of Wisdom

It is the responsibility of a disciple to take care of a:cha:rya's physical welfare. It is the major responsibility of the A:cha:rya to fulfill all spiritual needs of disciples.

Did You Know?

Lord Rangana:ttha is the first deity form of Supreme Lord on Earth.

Sri:rangam is the most ancient temple. It is located on the banks of the River Ka:ve:ri.

Lord Na:ra:ya**n**a gave this deity to Chathurmukha Bramha.

Later Bramha gave it to King Ikshva:ku, the ancestor of Lord Ra:ma.

Lord Rangana:ttha was worshipped by many generations in the Ikshava:ku dynasty. Ra:ma too prayed to Lord Rangana:ttha. After Ra:ma's coronation as the King of Ayo:dhya, He gave the deity to Vibhi:sha**n**a.

Vibhi:sha**n**a placed Rangana:ttha on the banks of the River Ka:ve:ri. To bless Vibhi:sha**n**a and his kingdom Lanka, Rangana:ttha faced south. Even today, we can see Him that way.

Ra:ma:nuja:cha:rya had two chefs. A:ndhrapu:r**n**a, also called Vaduganambi, boiled milk for Ra:ma:nuja:cha:rya. Pranatha:rthihara:cha:rya also called as Kida:mbi A:chcha:n, prepared food as recommended by Sri Gho:s**tt**i:pu:r**n**a. In fact, it was he who carried Ra:ma:nuja:cha:rya Swa:my on his back on the hot sand banks of Ka:ve:ri while Gho:s**tt**i:pu:r**n**a Swa:my came to visit.

5. OUR STRENGTH AND KNOWLEDGE IS FOR A:CHA:RYA SEVA ONLY

I. Choose the correct answer

1. A:runi
   a) was a great sage
   b) was a guru
   c) was a landlord
   d) wanted to learn sa:sthras

2. A:runi worked hard
   a) to serve and please his Guruji
   b) to save the crops
   c) to get some money
   d) to learn the scriptures

3. This story is from
   a) Maha:bha:ratha
   b) Ra:ma:yana
   c) Upanishads
   d) none of the above

4. While soaking in the rain.
   e) the crops were ruined
   f) guruji lost his way
   g) A:runi fell unconscious
   h) A:runi got strength

5. Guruji was concerned about
   a) his teachings
   b) the crop
   c) his a:sram
   d) his health

6. Guruji went to the field
   a) in search of A:runi
   b) to fetch some water
   c) to get fresh air
   d) to get some fruits

7. A:runi was able to control the water
   a) with mud
   b) by covering the breach with branches
   c) by lying down against the water flow
   d) none of the above

8. A:runi's hardwork
   a) is the quality of a good student
   b) is profitable
   c) is not good for health
   d) none of the above

9. The story of A:runi is an example for
   a) Ma:thrude:vo: bhava
   b) Pithrude:vo: bhava
   c) A:cha:ryade:vo: bhava
   d) Atthithide:vo: bhava

10. The moral of the story is
    a) serve your a:cha:rya
    b) to go and get wet in the rain
    c) save the crops
    d) obey your parents

II. True or False

1. A:runi was not unhappy while serving his guru.

2. Sage Dhaumya took care of his disciple.

3. A:runi became a world renowned scholar.

4. Sage Na:rada went to fields in search of A:runi.

5. Guruji fell unconscious in the fields.

III. Fill in the blanks

1. A:runi became a scholar in _____

2. A:runi stopped the _____flow.

3. Sage _____ was the guru of A:runi.

IV. Arrange the Sentences in Order

1. He blocked the flow with hands and feet.

2. He became unconscious.

3. It started raining heavily.

4. A:runi stopped the water flow with mud, branches, leaves.

5. Rain entered into fields.

6. Guru blessed A:runi.

7. Guru came and provided first-aid.

8. He sat against water flow.

V. Who said to Whom

1. "Don't worry"

2. "You blocked the flow of water."

VI. One Word Answers

1. Who went in search of A:runi ?

   _____

2. Where and how was A:runi found?

   _____

3. What did A:runi save?

   _____

VII. Answer the following

1. Explain gurubhakthi of A:runi.

   _____

   _____

2. What did A:runi achieve?

   _____

   _____

3. Why did sage Dhaumya bless A:runi?

   _____

   _____

4. Why was sage Dhaumya worried when it rained?

   _____

   _____

VIII. How many Sanskrit or English words can you make using letters from 'BRAMHA VIDYA'

IX. Find the odd one out

X. Let Us Learn

A guru is like a farmer

A farmer assesses the nature of the land. He removes the weeds, tills the land, and adds fertilizers if needed, to makes the land fertile for sowing the seeds to grow good crop. So also, a:cha:rya identifies the nature of the disciple. He removes bad behavior and bad thoughts and instills good qualities and good thoughts. He moulds the disciple into a good citgizen, making him fit for spiritual progress with charitable qualities to serve the community through righteous deeds.

Can you write 5 good qualities a guru instills in his disciple and 5 bad qualities he weeds out from him.

XI. Time Travel

Imagine you travelled back in time about 1000 years ago. Describe your classrooms through illustrations.

XII. Word Search

```
H L N O I S S A P M O C O A U
E A Q E N P U P I D Y Y X Q P
M B K Y C T O P B B K Y F U A
U Z E C I F I R C A S N V A S
O N O I S I C E D A O X D N A
P Y Y K I W S C W I L Y H T K
A K O R N F N I T A H V L O E
R O J I A K O A I T Q J K Y E
V Y S R C D C T Y N K R B U O
I Z Q Q Y I N E E H B H I O K
R E C E D E U U F Y R H A F C
H C A E R B B E O W B H A V W
Z C D R R E M E M B E R P V M
L B O B F I R B E X R U Z T U
Z T B U Y P B J M P S V G Z N
```

APPRECIATE   RECEDE

BOUNDARY   REMEMBER

BREACH   SACRIFICE

COMPASSION   TORRENTIAL

DECISION   UNCONSCIOUS

DEDICATION

XIII. Unscramble each of the clue words. Take the letters that appear in boxes and unscramble them for the final message.

NIAR

UMD

LODO

NIW

CORP

| | | V | E | |

XIV. Comprehension

Para:sara was a great sage. He wrote 'Vishnu Pura:nam'. Sage Para:sara and Sathyavathi gave birth to a son on an island in the river Ganges. An island is called 'dwi:pa' in Sanskrit. 'Ayanam' is the place of birth. Having been born in an island, the boy was named 'Dwaipa:yana'. His complexion was dark. Hence, his parents called him 'Krushna'. Taking these two factors into consideration, people recognized him as 'Krushna Dwaipa:yana'.

Krushna Dwaipa:yana learned the entire Ve:das from his father. Later, he left for Badrina:th and did a great penance. With the grace of Lord Badari Na:ra:yana, he divided the Ve:dic literature into four parts – Rug Ve:da, Yajur Ve:da, Sa:ma Ve:da and Attharva Ve:da. The task of classifying the entire Ve:dic literature is not an ordinary one. Only Godly people can do such a gigantic task. Since then, he

was recognized as Ve:da Vya:sa. Because he spent many months in Badrina:th, he was also known as Ba:dara:yana.He was renowned as Ve:da Vy:sa Ba:dara:yana by the scholars. His other works were

* 18 Maha: Pura:na:s, the stories of great kings and their lineages on this Earth

* Sriman Maha:bha:ratham – the history of human kind on this earth. It consists of 18 parva:s. The episode of A:runi is from the first parva.

* 545 Bramhasu:thras, the quintessence of all Upanishads.

All the documented literature that is available today is from Ve:da Vya:sa only. His birthday is considered as World Teacher's Day. It falls on A:sha:dha Pu:rnima of Lunar calendar. He became the Guru of Gurus because he was a perfect student and learnt everything from his guru i.e his father.

Let us try to become a perfect student like Ve:da Vy:sa Ba:dara:yana.

Questions

1. Who wrote Pura:nas?

   _____

2. When is World Teacher's Day?

   _____

3. Did the Holy Ve:das exist before Ve:da Vya:sa?

   _____

4. Where did Ve:da Vya:sa meditate?

   _____

5. Where did he write the scriptures?

   _____

6. What are the four Ve:das?

_____

7. Who were the parents of Dwaipa:yana?

_____

8. Who wrote Vishnu Pura:nam?

_____

9. What is the number and relevance of Bramhasu:thras?

_____

10. In which scripture do we find the story of Pa:ndavas and Kauravas?

_____

XV. Research

1. In regular schools, kids have a break every weekend. When do the kids at gurukulam have a break?

2. A modern school has a principal, clerks, janitor etc. Compare a modern day school's organizational structure to that of a gurukulam.

XVI. Guruji wants to reach A:runi . Show him the way.

XVII. Let us practice – Serve All Beings as Service to God

A:runi saved the crops of his guru from the flood. Here is a task for you too.

Your local VT Seva branch is creating a facility for 5 days to accommodate the flood victims. The victims should be provided with food and essential commodities. As VT Seva Secretary, you are in-charge of making sure that 100 kits are prepared by your team. Each kit will be given to a family of four members.

a) What materials are required to make a kit?

b) Mention the step-by-step process to complete this task successfully.

> ### Words of Wisdom
>
> Be rooted to the grace of guru. Cultivate faith and devotion within yourself. You will always reap the fruits of success.

Did you know?

Bramha Vidya: reveals the ultimate goal of life. Upanishads

discuss about the 32 processes of meditation. They are called 32 Bramha Vidyas or Para Vidyas. These scriptures discuss the details of the

Nature, the souls and the Supreme God and the means of discarding the karmic bondage of the soul. Though there are many scriptures available in the name of Upanishads, our a:cha:ryas mainly discussed about 14 Upanishads only. They are

i:sa ke:na katta prasna munda ma:ndu:kya thiththirihi
chha:ndo:gyam bruhada:ranyam aithare:yam dasaiva hi

Kaushi:thaki, swe:tha:svatharam, suba:la, maho:panishad, iso:panishad, ke:no:panishad, katto:panishad, prasno:panishad, mundako:panishad, ma:ndu:kya upanishad, thaiththiriyo:panishad, chha:ndo:gya upanishad, bruhada:ranyako:panishad, aithare:yo:panishad.

6. EVEN GOD FEELS INDEBTED TO HIS A:CHA:RYA

I. Choose the correct answer

1. Krushna and Balara:ma lived in

   a. Matthura

   b. Nandago:kulam

   c. Dwa:raka

   d. None of the above

2. Who killed Kamsa?

   a. Krushna

   b. Balara:ma

   c. Sa:ndi:pani

   d. Garga:cha:rya

3. 'akshara:bhya:sam' means

   a. initiation to education

   b. manthra initiation

   c. thanthra initiation

   d. all of the above

4. We have _____ varieties of arts.

   a. 24

   b. 54

   c. 64

   d. 8

5. Krushna searched for a:cha:rya

   a. to obtain formal education

   b. to study more

   c. to give gurudakshina

   d. none of the above

6. Krushna mastered all of the subjects in

    a. 6 years

    b. 6 months

    c. 1 year

    d. 64 days

7. Sa:ndi:pani's wife wished

    a. to get wealth and prosperity

    b. to get back her sons alive

    c. to get mo:ksha (salvation)

    d. all of the above

8. Krushna wanted formal education

    a. to become an expert

    b. to set a right example to human beings

    c. as he forgot everything

    d. both a and b

9. What should one ask God?

    a. wealth and fame

    b. health

    c. children

    d. everlasting happiness

    e. Nothing! the knows better

10. Krushna and Balara:ma showed gratitude to Sa:ndi:pani

    a. by giving gurudakshina

    b. by ordering Yama

    c. by learning well

    d. all of the above

II. Fill in the blanks

1. _____ can change many bodies like we change our clothes.

2. The soul takes up a body to perform its _____

3. Relationships are limited to the _____ and not to the soul.

4. Soul is _____ while the body is temporary.

5. One should give priority to what is _____.

III. State True or False

1. Krushna and Balara:ma came to Matthura for Dhanurya:ga.

2. Sa:ndipani did akshara:bhya:sam to Krushna and Balara:ma.

3. Sage Garga:cha:rya taught Krushna and Balara:ma.

4. Everyone should learn from a:cha:rya.

5. All of us should show gratitude towards our teachers.

6. Sri Krushna spent his childhood in Matthura.

7. Balara:ma gave gurudakshina to Garga:cha:rya.

8. Sri Krushna learned 16 arts in 64 days.

9. Sa:ndi:pani asked for a very trivial boon.

10. It was Sa:ndi:pani's wish to get back his dead sons alive.

IV. Match the following

1. Gurukulam was   Lord Krushna's brother
2. Lord Krushna   imprisoned Krushna's parents
3. Balara:ma   Jagadguru
4. Kamsa   place where Krushna and Balara:ma grew
5. Nandago:kulam   on the banks of river Ganga

V. Correct the Spellings

1. Nandagokulam

2. Bhagvan

3. Sandpani

4. chatusasti kalapurna

5. akashurabhysm

6. samdra

7. Yuma

8. Dhanus yagna

VI. Who said to Whom

1. 'What can I teach him?' _____

2. 'Let us know what would please you?' _____

3. 'That itself is a best tribute.' _____

4. 'We are honored by your love and affection.' _____

VII. Who am I?

1. All sinners come to my place. I am the king of that place. Who am I?

2. We were six brothers who used to live in Yama Lo:ka. All of a sudden, we were sent to Earth. Who were we?

3. I am holy. Once these six young boys came to take bath but never returned to my shore. Who am I?

4. I am wide and deep. Many living beings and treasures exist in me. Lord Ra:ma as well as Lord Krushna ordered me to do something and I obeyed their orders because they were my bosses. Who am I?

5. I invited Krushna and Balara:ma to Dhanur Ya:ga to finish them. Who am I?

6. I am on the bank of River Ganga. Lord Krushna stayed here along with his brother to study. Who am I?

VIII. Rearrange the Sentences in order

1. Yama obeyed Krushna's orders and quickly brought the children. _____

2. He immediately rushed to his wife with joy. _____

3. Krushna is an incarnation. _____

4. Since He took birth as a human being, He wanted to behave as one too. _____

5. They blessed Krushna and Balara:ma to become the saviors of the world. _____

6. Please bring back our children who were drowned at the Prabha:sa thi:rttha. _____

7. Krushna summoned Samudra. _____

8. His wife knew that Krushna was God incarnate and could do anything. _____

9. His a:sram was in Ka:si. _____

10. A:cha:rya was humbled by their request. _____

IX. Short Answers

1. Which yajna did Kamsa perform?

_____

2. What is the master of 64 arts called?

_____

3. Whom did Krushna summon to know the whereabouts of kids?

_____

4. Who was the master of 64 arts?

_____

5. Who was Krushna's brother?

_____

6. What was Krushna's age at the time of akshara:bhya:sam?

_____

7. Where was Sa:ndi:pani's a:sram located?

_____

8. Where did the six children drown?

_____

9. What is the nature of the soul?

_____

10. Where were the guru's kids?

_____

11. What is 'sea' called in Sanskrit?

_____

12. Who invited the two brothers to Matthura?

_____

13. When does the learning process of a man end?

_____

14. What gurudakshina did Krushna and Balara:ma give to their teacher?

_____

15. Describe Krushna's reaction after knowing the wish of his guru.

_____

X. Answer the following

1. Where did Sri: Krushna spend his childhood?

_____

_____

2. Is Nature a teacher? Explain.

_____

_____

3. Write a few lines about Sa:ndi:pani.

_____

_____

4. Why did Sri: Krushna continue his education in Ka:si?

_____

_____

5. What did Sri: Krushna's guru wish for? Why?

_____

_____

6. Krushna also gave gurudakshina. Explain

_____

_____

7. Explain the importance of a:cha:rya.

_____

_____

8. Whom did Sri: Krushna release from prison?

_____

_____

XI. How many Sanskrit or English words can you make using letters from 'CHATUSHSHASHTI KALA:PU:RNA'

XII. Let Us Learn
a) Guru is like the Mother Earth.

Many species exist on Mother Earth. Among these thousands of species, only we human beings misuse natural resources and spoil Nature. We cause tremendous harm to Mother Earth. We release toxic and radioactive wastes into the atmosphere, drill gas from the earth, use non biodegradable products such as plastic, and cause ozone depletion.

But, for our survival, Mother Earth bears all our misdeeds with a lot of patience. It is only because of her forbearance that we are able to live.

A guru too is like Mother Earth. Most of the disciples are egoistic, arrogant, jealous, selfish etc… A guru, with all of his patience and tutelage, works on removing the bad qualities from his disciples and makes them better citizens.

b)   Process of approaching a guru

thadviddhi pranipa:the:na

pariprasne:na se:vaya: |

upade:kshyanthi the: jna:nam

jna:nina sthathva darsinaha || 34

Lord Krushna in Bhagawad Gi:tha *(Chapter 4, 34 slo:ka)* said

* A disciple should be submissive, humble and free from ego.
* A disciple must be inquisitive and wait for the appropriate time to ask relevant questions.
* A disciple must help the teacher as and when required.

XIII. Find the odd one out

XIV. Word Search

```
O N I K A X L B O F C N C J X
O O D M E A G E R N O U H R I
W I E H X X M P F S Z V E E N
P T T A E T U B I R T A R N Q
W A A O M V E R Y B C U I O U
H R R X P P P P N C T H S W I
P E T T L M M P O A C K H N R
T P S U I P W L M O C V C E E
X O N S F C A M H S L A V D U
S O O X I D I D E P R I V E K
L C M S E L L P T N A Y V C T
X R E S D P J V A N Q U I S H
T F D U M K L T B T C V T O Q
J W K V E L E V A T E T A B J
T P A Z W N M W K R O I V A S
```

ACCOLADES

CHERISH

COOPERATION

DEMONSTRATE

DEPRIVE

ELEVATE

EXEMPLIFIED

IMMATURE

IMPRISON

INCARNATE

INQUIRE

MEAGER

PARTICIPATE

RENOWNED

SAVIOR

TRIBUTE

VANQUISH

XV. Sa:ndipani's sons are coming back from Yama Lo:ka. Can you help them find the way?

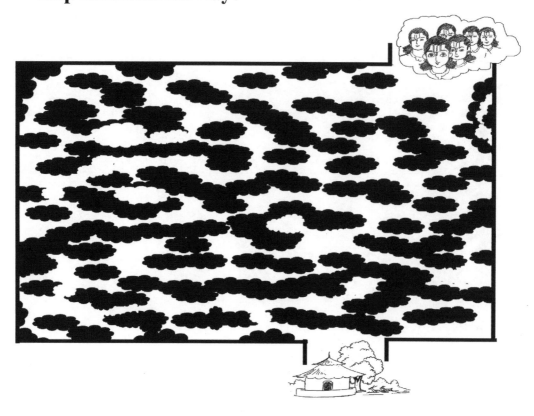

XVI. Unscramble each of the clue words.

Copy the letters in the numbered cells to other cells with the same number.

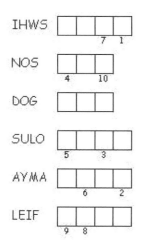

IHWS   ☐ ☐ ☐ ☐
             7   1

NOS   ☐ ☐ ☐
         4   10

DOG   ☐ ☐ ☐

SULO   ☐ ☐ ☐ ☐
          5   3

AYMA   ☐ ☐ ☐ ☐
            6   2

LEIF   ☐ ☐ ☐ ☐
         9   8

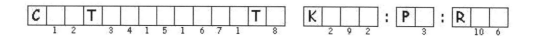

C ☐ T ☐ ☐ ☐ ☐ ☐ T ☐   K ☐ ☐ : P ☐ : R ☐ ☐
1 2   3 4 1 5 1 6 7 1 8   2 9 2   3   10 6

XVII. Complete the Family Tree of Lord Krushna

XVIII. Research

    1. Process of akshara:bhya:sam?

    2. Gurus of Lord Vishnu in his various avatha:ras

    3. Compare and contrast the modern education system with the one
       in a gurukulam.

> ## *Words of Wisdom*
>
> *Every day is a learning experience.*
> *Cherish every moment and every lesson*
> *and show your gratitude to all your*
> *teachers – both human and Nature.*

XIX. Let us practice - Serve all beings as service to God

Krushna grew up on the banks of River Yamuna and studied by the banks of river Ganga. Nowadays rivers are getting polluted. Cleaning the rivers helps Mother Earth to support life for a long time. VT Seva observes Earth Day on April 22nd . Your school decided to spend the whole day serving Mother Earth. Your teacher announced that whoever comes up with the best project for Earth Day will be announced as "Student of the Month". Propose at least 3 Earth Day related projects.

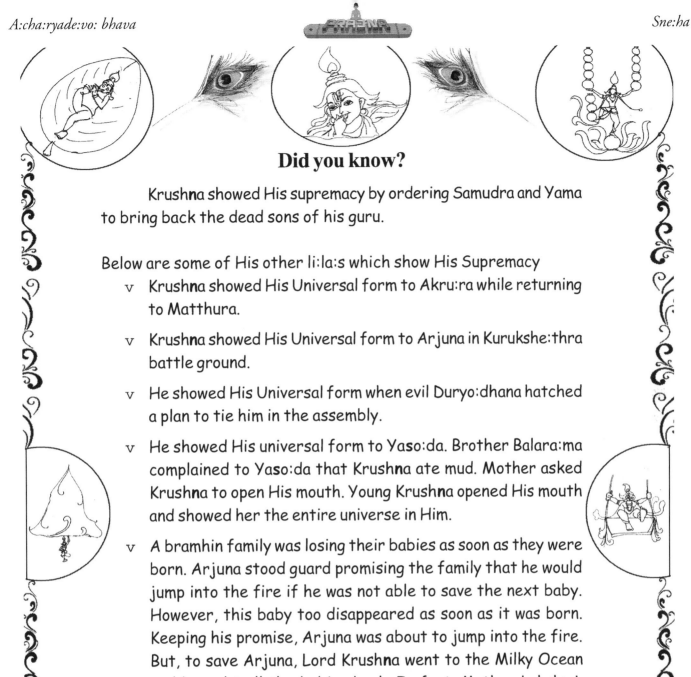

Did you know?

Krushna showed His supremacy by ordering Samudra and Yama to bring back the dead sons of his guru.

Below are some of His other li:la:s which show His Supremacy

- v Krushna showed His Universal form to Akru:ra while returning to Matthura.

- v Krushna showed His Universal form to Arjuna in Kurukshe:thra battle ground.

- v He showed His Universal form when evil Duryo:dhana hatched a plan to tie him in the assembly.

- v He showed His universal form to Yaso:da. Brother Balara:ma complained to Yaso:da that Krushna ate mud. Mother asked Krushna to open His mouth. Young Krushna opened His mouth and showed her the entire universe in Him.

- v A bramhin family was losing their babies as soon as they were born. Arjuna stood guard promising the family that he would jump into the fire if he was not able to save the next baby. However, this baby too disappeared as soon as it was born. Keeping his promise, Arjuna was about to jump into the fire. But, to save Arjuna, Lord Krushna went to the Milky Ocean and brought all the babies back. In fact, Mother Lakshmi, curious to see her spouse, took all the babies. Krushna, knowing this, went to His abode, said hi to Her, and returned with all the disappeared children.

This Supreme Lord, who showed His True Form many a time, became a disciple and showed that everyone needs an A:cha:rya. The all powerful Supreme Lord was not only an obedient student but served His a:cha:rya with devotion. Let us all become true disciples like Him and serve our a:cha:rya with love and devotion!

7. SINCERE SERVICE IS REWARDED APPROPRIATELY

I. Choose the correct answer

1. The truths of the Universe were discovered by
   a. ve:dic sages
   b. kings
   c. de:vathas
   d. God

2. Sathyaka:ma
   a. was a kulapathi
   b. was Upako:sala's guru
   c. was a Vedic student
   d. was Upako:sala's father

3. Thre:tha:gni means
   a. 5 fires
   b. 3 fires
   c. 30 fires
   d. 8 fires

4. Thre:tha:gni should be protected
   a. till the wood is burnt
   b. till the end of the ya:ga
   c. life long
   d. till evening

5. Sages meditated on manthras to
   a. find peace
   b. find ultimate truths
   c. for concentration
   d. to get boons

6. Sages congregate at places

    a. to exchange and get consensus on results of meditation

    b. to feast during festivals

    c. for group meditation

    d. for student exchange program

7. Upako:sala heard a human voice from the

    a. sky

    b. fire

    c. water

    d. God

8. Which manthra did the fires reveal

    a. kham brahma brahma kam

    b. kham kham: bramha bramha:

    c. kam bramha: kham bramha:

    d. kam brahma: kham brahma:

9. Devotion should lead to

    a. faith

    b. service

    c. realization

    d. bliss

10. Upako:sala passed the test of

    a. perseverance

    b. patience

    c. devotion

    d. faith

II. Fill in the blanks

1. The three fires are called _____ , _____ and _____

2. One who is God-realized is called _____

3. Upako:sala approached Sathyaka:ma to acquire _____

4. There are _____ bramhavidyas.

5. If sacred fires get extinguished, _____ activities must be observed.

III. True or False

1. Upako:sala did not like his guru.

2. Guru's wife took care of fires occasionally.

3. Dakshina:gni is one of the ritualistic fires.

4. Sathyaka:ma was jealous of Upako:sala.

5. Service without any expectations or irrations bestows real knowledge.

IV. Match Defintions

gurukulam	Knowledge of Supreme and steps to attain the Supreme
kulapathi	God realized
bramha jna:na	a particular process of meditation
bramhave:ththa	ritualistic fire of a household in three forms
thre:tha:gni	head of gurukulam
bramhavidya:	a residential facility for seekers to learn, meditate, and decide the Ultimate Truths

V. Who said to Whom

1. 'Kam Bramha kham Bramha!' _____

2. 'How can I please my guru?' _____

3. 'God is instructing me through the fires to initiate the child.'

   _____

4. 'We are satisfied with your selfless service.' _____

5. 'May I know the meaning please?' _____

6. 'You seem to be a realized soul!' _____

7. 'Don't get disappointed.' _____

8. 'Your guru will show you the rest.' _____

VI. Who am I?

1. We are very sacred. Ve:dic people offer ghee, wood, etc in us using manthras. Upako:sala took very good care of us. Who are we?

   _____

2. I am very powerful. Agni de:vatha gave me to Upako:sala. He meditated and got the grace of guru. Who am I?

   _____

3. This boy in the a:sram was very dedicated. However, he was always sad. I used to console him. Who am I?

   _____

4. I am one of the 32 vidya:s. I was named after this great disciple. Who am I?

   _____

5. I am a central hub. Many Vedic people come here to discuss their experiences. Even students join here and learn bramhavidya. However, not everyone is lucky enough to get that knowledge. Who am I?

VII. Arrange the sentences in order

1. That bramhavidya: became famous as Upako:sala Vidya:.

2. Upako:sala approached him for Bramhavidya.

3. Guru tested the dedication of Upako:sala.

4. Fires gave him a manthra.

5. Guru's wife asked Guru to bless Upako:sala with knowledge.

6. Sathyaka:ma was a bramhave:ththa.

7. Upako:sala started meditating on manthra.

8. Guru saw a glow in Upako:sala's face.

9. Guru initiated Upako:sala the ultimate knowledge.

10. Upako:sala started taking care of a:havani:ya, ga:rhapathya, dakshina:gni.

VIII. Correct the spellings

1. Sathyakama
2. Kulupati
3. Bramhaveta
4. Upmakosa
5. Bramhagnana
6. Trupta:gni
7. Dakshinigni
8. Ahavaniya
9. Garhapathy
10. Upakosala vida

IX. Short Answers

1. Who was Sathyaka:ma?

   _____

2. What was Sathyaka:ma's speciality?

   _____

3. Who approached Sathyaka:ma?

   _____

4. What is the head of a gurukulam called?

   _____

5. What did Upako:sala protect?

   _____

6. What made Upako:sala stay for a long time in the a:sram?

   _____

7. Who was like a mother to Upako:sala?

   _____

8. Who appeared before Upako:sala?

_____

9. How long is the pursuit for truth?

_____

10. Why was a bramhavidya: named Upako:sala Vidya?

_____

X. Answer the following

1. Why was Upako:sala unhappy?

_____

_____

2. What was Upako:sala's daily routine?

_____

_____

3. What does thre:tha:gni mean? Name them.

_____

_____

4. When did Upako:sala's guru initiate him?

_____

_____

5. What favor did the fires do to Upako:sala?

_____

_____

6. When does one obtain real knowledge?

_____

_____

XI.   Let Us Learn

Learn from the Moon

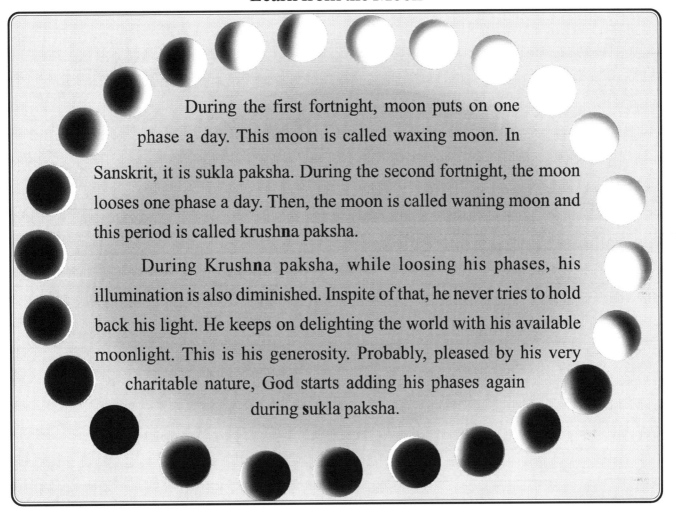

During the first fortnight, moon puts on one phase a day. This moon is called waxing moon. In Sanskrit, it is sukla paksha. During the second fortnight, the moon looses one phase a day. Then, the moon is called waning moon and this period is called krushna paksha.

During Krushna paksha, while loosing his phases, his illumination is also diminished. Inspite of that, he never tries to hold back his light. He keeps on delighting the world with his available moonlight. This is his generosity. Probably, pleased by his very charitable nature, God starts adding his phases again during sukla paksha.

Do not be deprived of your nature of helping others. Even if you loose a little, God is great. He protects your charitable nature and provides you the needed resources.

XII.   How many Sanskrit or English words can you make using letters from 'UPAKO:SALA VIDYA:'

XIII. Complete the steps for attaining bliss

XIV. Unscramble each of the clue words. Copy the letters in the numbered cells to other cells with the same number.

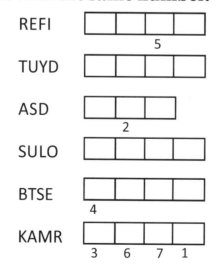

REFI   ☐☐☐☐ (5)

TUYD   ☐☐☐☐

ASD   ☐☐☐ (2)

SULO   ☐☐☐☐

BTSE   ☐☐☐☐ (4)

KAMR   ☐☐☐☐ (3 6 7 1)

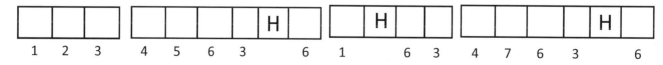

| 1 | 2 | 3 | | 4 | 5 | 6 | 3 | | 6 | | 1 | H | | 6 | 3 | | 4 | 7 | 6 | 3 | | 6 |

XV. Identify whose activities are real "Services"

1. "Gosh! It's almost Friday evening! I volunteered to complete this work to please my boss but I still have a lot to do! I wish I could go to a movie instead of working over the weekend."

2. "Hey Yash! Why don't you volunteer? You will get admission into a good college if you do some community service."

3. "Prathik! Why are you volunteering? You will get nothing out of it". "Arjun, I love what I do. I cannot stop myself from serving. I don't know these folks but they really need some help. I am glad that I am able to do something for them."

4. "Ansh! Don't worry, I will complete this volunteer task for you though I am busy."

XVI. A true disciple's quality

In olden days , when having food, one did not use glasses for drinking water. Water was directly poured to the mouth. Once, Bhagawad Ra:ma:nuja's disciple, Kida:mbi Achcha:n, was serving food to devotees. While taking prasadam, an old devotee requested for some water. Kida:mbi Aa:chcha:n poured water in the old man's mouth. However, while drinking, the old man choked. Bhagawad Ra:ma:nuja got angry and chided Kida:mbi for his careless act in the presence of everyone.

Kida:mbi A:chcha:n did not feel insulted. Instead, he prostrated before his a:cha:rya, and in all humility, quoted a song sung by sage Nammalva:r, "panima:nam pizhaiya:me: adiye:nai pani konda:i", which means "You corrected and put me in the right process of service when I crossed the line."

Let us also take any lesson positively, not getting hurt when elders correct us.

What's wrong in the picture

XVII. Find the odd one out

XVIII. Word Search

```
P  G  E  Y  B  E  Q  C  R  E  M  P  G  W  D
A  Y  B  C  V  R  I  O  M  E  V  M  Z  Y  C
T  M  E  P  N  L  D  N  K  Y  V  T  P  B  I
I  V  S  O  T  A  X  G  I  T  X  E  W  P  T
E  T  T  R  W  N  R  R  N  T  L  X  A  V  S
N  I  O  L  R  G  E  E  S  A  I  N  K  L  I
C  U  W  P  W  U  M  G  V  K  K  A  F  R  L
E  S  H  L  F  T  A  A  I  E  M  Q  T  G  A
I  R  S  P  I  L  U  T  V  L  S  F  A  E  U
R  U  T  M  T  X  A  I  B  W  I  R  F  N  T
I  P  M  A  Y  E  R  O  L  L  J  D  E  P  I
V  O  R  L  S  V  E  N  T  R  U  S  T  P  R
C  E  G  A  L  E  T  U  T  C  D  R  G  F  Z
E  L  B  A  M  O  H  T  A  F  N  U  S  J  K
W  V  F  O  U  Z  P  R  O  S  T  R  A  T  E
```

ALTAR	PATIENCE
BESTOW	PERSEVERANCE
COMMITMENT	PROSTRATE
CONGREGATION	PURSUIT
DILIGENT	REVEAL
ENTRUST	RITUALISTIC
INITIATE	TUTELAGE
LORE	UNFATHOMABLE

XIX. Sathyaka:ma lost his way while coming back to gurukulam. Can you help him find the way?

XX. Time Travel

Imagine you were a teacher of war-fare in gurukulam about 5000 years ago. What would your daily routine be? What would you teach the students?

XXI. Let us Practice - Serve all Beings as Service to God

Its lunch time. Imagine there is a fire in your school cafetaria. Many students are trapped or need first-aid. You are a VT Seva Volunteer Coordinator for Emergency Response Team. Currently, you have 25 volunteers in your team. How will you contact your team officers to volunteer in the rescue operations? List at least three different ways of contacting them and conducting the rescue operations.

XXII. Comprehension

"chathur" means four, and "ma:sam" means month. The four months during Cha:thurma:syam are considered as God's resting time because He meditates in Yo:ganidra. The wise always realize and feel the presence of God in their hearts. Hence, the Gurus do not move around much to avoid disturbance to the Lord who resides in their hearts. They stay in one place, starting from A:sha:**dh**a Pu:**rn**ima for four months. We worship our Gurus on A:sha:**dh**a Pu:**rn**ima day.

It is rainy season during this time of the year. Many varieties of life are born at this time. Aware of this, the Gurus practice austerities and reside in one place to avoid disturbance to the upcoming life on the ground. This shows their concern for life on Earth and the environment. During this period, they bless their disciples and devotees with divine messages and knowledge that they have accumulated over time.

Fill in the blanks

1. Chathur means _____.

2. Ma:sam means _____.

3. God resides in guru's _____.

4. Gurus don't move during four months showing concern to _____.

5. Gurus bless everyone with _____ during this time.

XXIII. Research

1. Types of sacred fires and their names

2. We have 8 directions viz east, west, south etc. In each direction, a de:vatha resides. In which corner does Agni reside? Who resides in the other directions?

3. Names of few Bramha Vidyas.

Words of Wisdom

It is only the service without any expectations or irritation that bestows real knowledge.

Did you know?

Nowadays, almost all houses have fireplaces. We use fire to keep ourselves warm and cozy during winters. We also have bon fires during weekends for fun. In olden days, people considered fire very sacred. All the offerings to de:vathas were given through Fire. Ve:dic people had altars with sacred fire in their houses. They maintained the ritualistic fires very carefully with a lot of devotion and dedication. The smoke from these sacred fires has medicinal value. Such fires do not spoil the environment. Instead, they play a role in getting adequate rainfall. These sacred fires also purify the atmosphere. These smokes control air pollution as well. Lord Krushna adviced us to do ya:gas or support such activities to please the natural divine forces around us.

---

8. VISWA:MITHRA

I. Choose the correct answer

1. Viswa:mithra did _____ in four directions.

    a. penance

    b. puja

    c. travel

    d. war

2. Siddhi means

    a. doing penance in four directions

    b. becoming a monarch

    c. doing good work

    d. dedicating everything at lotus feet of Lord

3. Viswa:mithra did yajna

    a. for 6 nights

    b. for ultimate siddhi

    c. in Siddha:srama

    d. all of the above

4. Ma:ri:cha and Suba:hu are

    a. de:vathas

    b. demons

    c. kings

    d. sages

5. Viswa:mithra

    a. did Ra:ma 10 favors

    b. performed Ra:ma's marriage

    c. did penance in four directions

    d. all of the above

6. Bala and Athibala are

    a. two demons

    b. two manthras

    c. brothers

    d. sons of Ra:ma

7. Ra:ma broke

    a. **S**iva Dhanus

    b. Vish**n**u Dhanus

    c. Bramha Dhanus

    d. Viswa:mithra Dhanus

8. Ra:ma released

    a. Ahalya from curse

    b. arrows

    c. prisoner Ma:ri:cha

    d. Parasura:ma

9. Vish**n**u dhanus was brought by

    a. Viswa:mithra

    b. **S**iva

    c. Vasishtta

    d. Parasura:ma

10. Vishwa:mithra =

    a. vishwa: + mithra

    b. viswa + mithra

    c. viswam+ mithra

    d. vishnu + mithra

II. Fill in the blanks

1. Ra:ma killed _____ and threw _____ with ease.

2. The yajna was for _____days.

3. The ability to withdraw weapons is called_____.

4. With bala and athibala, Ra:ma conquered _____ and sleep.

5. Dhanus sa:sthra has asthras and _____

6. Viswa:mithra conquered _____ in southern corner.

7. Viswa:mithra conquered _____ in eastern corner.

8. Viswa:mithra conquered _____ in northern corner.

9. Viswa:mithra conquered _____ in western corner.

10. Viswa:mithra wanted to provide Ra:ma ___ unparallel benefits.

III. True or False

1. Meditation makes a man perfect.

2. Mundane benefits are alluring.

3. Viswa:mithra was Krushna's guru.

4. Viswa:mithra was doing yajna for siddhi.

5. Ma:ri:cha and Suba:hu interrupted the yajna.

6. Tha:taka was Ra:vana's sister.

7. Viswa:mithra took Ra:ma to Siddha:sra:ma.

8. Ahalya was cursed to become a tree.

9. Viswa:mithra took Ra:ma to Mitthila: kingdom.

10. Ra:ma defeated Parasura:ma and took the Siva bow.

IV. Match the following

1. Krushna   A. Dro:**na**
2. Balara:ma   B. Va**s**ishtta
3. Upamanyu   C. Sa:ndi:pani
4. Ra:ma   D. Sathyaka:ma
5. Pa:ndavas and Kauravas   E. Dhaumya
6. Upako:sala
7. A:ru**ni**

V. Who said to Whom

1. 'Command us with no hesitation.'

   _____

2. 'I will fulfill it.'

   _____

3. 'Do not hesitate.'

   _____

4. 'Ra:ma will be safe under his shade.'

   _____

5. 'Only Ra:ma can conquer them.'

   _____

VI. Correct the Spellings

1. Ravana   6. Goothama
2. Vishumithra   7. Mitila
3. Subuhu   8. Acharyadevbhav
4. Marishcha   9. Dasarata
5. Alahya   10. Vasista

VII. Rearrange the sentences in order

1. Ra:ma went to Mitthila: kingdom. _____

2. Ra:ma killed Suba:hu _____

3. Ra:ma married Si:tha. _____

4. Viswa:mithra completed the yajna and got siddhi. _____

5. Guru gave all asthra:s to Ra:ma _____

6. Viswa:mithra got rid of ego. _____

7. Viswa:mithra got rid of hunger. _____

8. Ra:ma won Vishnu Dhanus. _____

9. Viswa:mithra got rid of anger. _____

10. Viswa:mithra got rid of lust. _____

11. Ra:ma broke Siva Dhanus. _____

12. Ahalya was rid of her curse. _____

13. Ra:ma and Lakshmana went to Siddha:sra:ma. _____

14. Ra:ma was 13 years old. _____

15. Viswa:mithra came to Dasarattha's assembly. _____

VIII. Who am I?

1. I am an old demoness. A young handsome boy came to fight me. Who am I?

2. Many sages came to my place to do a yajna. However, two demons were always putting bad stuff and spoiling it. Finally, two young boys came to my rescue. Who am I?

3. The most handsome guy won the challenge and married me. Who am I?

4. I am a real friend to the entire world. Who am I?

5. Ra:ma shot an arrow at me and I was thrown thousands of miles away by its force. Who am I?

IX. One Word Answers

1. What did Viswa:mithra teach Ra:ma?

    _____

2. Who arrived at Dasarattha's assembly?

    _____

3. At what age did Ra:ma accompany Viswa:mithra?

    _____

4. Who convinced Dasarattha?

    _____

5. Whose bow was broken by Ra:ma?

    _____

6. Who accompanied Ra:ma?

    _____

7. Who was expert in asthras?

   _____

8. Who was Ra:ma's first target?

   _____

9. What is the ability to withdraw asthras called?

   _____

10. Who was lying as dust since ages?

    _____

11. Whose bow was displayed in Mitthila: ?

    _____

12. From whom did Ra:ma win the bow?

    _____

13. How is Ra:ma worshipped?

    _____

14. Whose son was Viswa:mithra?

    _____

X. Answer the following

1. How was Ra:ma's strength displayed to the world?

   _____

   _____

2. What did the Holy Ve:das instruct?

   _____

   _____

3. How did Vasishtta convince Dasarattha?

_____

_____

4. What is ultimate siddhi?

_____

_____

5. Ra:ma is a true disciple. Explain.

_____

_____

XI. How many Sanskrit and English words can you make with "ASTHRA UPASAMHA:RA"

.

XII. Find atleast 10 differences

XIII. Let Us Learn

Qualities of an a:cha:rya

* A:cha:rya does the following

* a:chino:thi – gathers all the secrets from the scriptures

* a:cha:re: sttha:payathi — passes the knowledge to the seekers and makes them practice.

* swayam a:charathe: — he practices what he preaches

* A:cha:rya is one who mastered the Ve:dic knowledge.

* A:cha:rya does not have jealousy. He feels happy, appreciates the progress of others, and encourages them.

* A:cha:rya is a realized soul who practices manthra, is hooked to God and is subservient to the lineage of the gurus.

* In the scripture Sri:vachana Bhu:shanam, Pillai Lo:ka:cha:rya clearly defines the qualities of an a:cha:rya.

  "A true a:cha:rya is the one who has the above qualities. He should come from a:cha:rya lineage and initiate the truth seekers with the 'King of Manthras' i.e "Ashta:kshari: Manthra"

XIV. Word Search

```
Q B Z S L A S Z I F M S D Z S
O A A O M I E H S O U D P W C
L E V I U H I B E S T O W H V
Z Z L E Y G T M L T N I B X B
E X E M P L I F Y V L N X T X
O B X O G T C T N A S T C S R
M V J L T A O A R L E E L N K
W R E H K A R H I G T N I D V
Z P I R Q L T I A W A T H E W
D L V T W S A T H V O I C S F
A H T X A H I Z W D Z O V O J
N D A A M M E L I D D N N P F
I P L N R U C L I O Q I I M Q
X C F E U B L E M I B V S I F
U F H Y H S R K E Q S N L G A
```

ASTHRA

ATROCITIES

BESTOW

DHANUS

DILEMMA

EXEMPLIFY

HERMITAGE

IMPOSE

INTENTION

MITTHILA

OVERWHELM

SIDDHI

XV. Unscramble

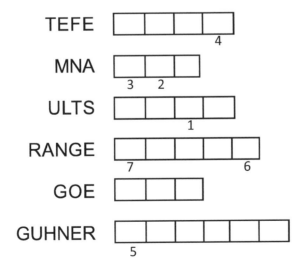

TEFE ☐☐☐☐ (4)

MNA ☐☐☐ (3)(2)

ULTS ☐☐☐☐ (1)

RANGE ☐☐☐☐☐ (7)(6)

GOE ☐☐☐

GUHNER ☐☐☐☐☐☐ (5)

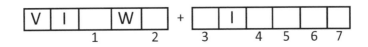

V I ☐ W ☐ + ☐ I ☐ ☐ ☐ ☐
1   2   3   4 5 6 7

XVI. Time Travel

Imagine you were one of the sages performing the yajna along with Viswa:mithra. Describe the fight you witnessed between the demons and Ra:ma & Lakshmana.

XVII. Research

1. Observe your surroundings. Write at least 3 points on what you learn from 3 of them.

2. Compare the dress code in modern schools with the dress code in gurukulams.

XVIII. Complete the Family Tree of Sri Ra:ma

Words of Wisdom

Realize that every object in the Universe is the divine body of God in that particular form. Holy Ve:da instructed us to worship guru on par with God in this manthra.

yasya de:ve: para: bhakthihi yattha: de:ve: thattha: gurow

thasyaithe: katthitha:hyarttha:ha praka:santhe: maha:thmanaha

One should have unshakable faith in God. Same intensity of faith should be there in the guru too. Then the Holy Ve:das themselves will open the doors to such devotees to unfold the hidden secrets.

Did you know?

Our scripture says…..'*acha:ryasthu haris sa:ksha:th chara ru:pi:na samsayaha*' It means, 'A Guru is visible form of God that moves.'

Everybody on Earth needs a spiritual Guru to obtain the real knowledge. Even Lord Ra:ma and Lord Krushna had gurus. Lord Ra:ma's gurus were Sage Vasishtta and Sage Viswa:mithra . Lord Krushna's gurus were Sage Garga and Sage Sa:ndi:pani.

Lord in Archa: also accepted a:cha:rya.

Bhagawad Ra:ma:nuja:cha:rya once went to Thirukkurungudi, Kuranga Nagari. There, the Lord is called 'Thirukkurungudi Nambi'. One day, Lord asked Ra:ma:nuja:cha:rya, "How can you manage to have so many devotees as your followers?" Ra:ma:nuja:cha:rya replied, "I possess the ' manthra rathna' which is like a precious gem among all the manthras. It is not bound by any restrictions. With its power the people are influenced." Then, Lord Thirukkurungudi Nambi asked Ra:ma:nuja:cha:rya to initiate Him with that manthra. Ra:ma:nuja:cha:rya was offered a gold chair. The Lord sat in front of him and received the manthra. Thus Lord in archa: became Ra:ma:nuja:cha:rya's disciple.

In Thirumala, Lord Venkate:swara became the disciple of Bhagawad Ra:ma:nuja:cha:rya after taking the Sankha and Chakra from Ra:manuja:cha:rya. Lord commanded Anantha:lva:n to consecrate Ra:ma:nuja:cha:rya's deity in the temple on a raised platform such that the feet of Bhagawad Ra:ma:nuja:cha:rya should be at the level of his heart. Observe this when you go to Thirumala next time!

In Sri:rangam, Lord Rangana:ttha too felt that He needed a:cha:rya. After hearing Manava:la Maha:muni's narration on 1000 songs of Nammalva:r called Bhagavad Vishayam , Lord appeared as a boy and offered a couplet as gurudakshina. Then, He disappeared into the main temple. Even today, in all the divya de:sams and houses, any prayer or any event is started with this couplet which was offered by Lord Rangana:ttha to Manava:la Maha:Muni.

sri:saile:sa daya:pa:thram dhi:bhakthya:di guna:rnavam |
yathi:ndra pravanam vande: ramya ja:ma:tharam munim ||

SUMMARY QUESTIONS ON "A:CHA:RYA DEVO: BHAVA" SERIES

1. We have seen 5 disciples in "**A:cha:rya De:vo Bhava**" series of stories (other than God himself playing the role of a **Sishya**). They are Arjuna, Upamanyu, A:runi, A:ndhra Pu:rna and Upako:sala. Each one of them showed us a unique and exceptional quality in serving A:cha:rya. Which quality did each disciple show?

Qualites we can learn from disciples	How was he tested or proved	Comments
Arjuna	A:cha:ryadevo:bhava	
Upamanyu		
A:runi		
A:ndhra Pu:rna		
Upako:sala		

2. There are mainly 3 kinds of A:cha:ryas. Can you find out what they are and how are they classified? (**Hint:** "Krupa:ma:thra Prasanna:charya" is one and the **rarest** of all...)

3. Our Swamiji **H.H. Tridandi Chinna Jeeyar Swamiji** falls into the category of "Krupa:ma:thra Prasanna:cha:rya.." easily. Can you think of some examples that could prove this? Particularly think about H.H. grace when He himself travels across the globe to reach out to the many in need and extend His blessings...!!!!

SNE:HA

so:ka:ra:thi bhaya thra:nam pri:thi visrambha bha:janam |
ke:na srushtam idam rathnam 'mithram' ithyakshara dwayam ? ||

'Oh! Who created this priceless two syllable gem called <u>"sne:ha"</u> which protects from fear of miseries and enemies, and which is The Abode of Love and Faith? It must be GOD'.

1. INTRODUCTION

I. Fill in the blanks

1. Cohesiveness among living creatures is called _____ in Sanskrit.

2. Rasa:bha:sa leads to _____.

3. Friendship for personal benefit _____.

4. Ra:ma said to _____, "e:kam duhkham sukham cha nau".

5. Man shares his _____ with his friends.

II. Answer the following

1. What is uththama sne:ha?

   _____

2. How does a true friend help?

   _____

3. An oil lamp is an example of true friendship. How?

   _____

4. Describe friendship with selfish people using a simile.

   _____

5. Describe the importance of friendship in your own words.

   _____

III. Explain the following Sanskrit terms

1. "e:kam duhkham sukham cha nau"
2. Rasa:bha:sa
3. Uththama sne:ha
4. Sne:ha

IV. Label the types of 'sne:ham' in the pictures below

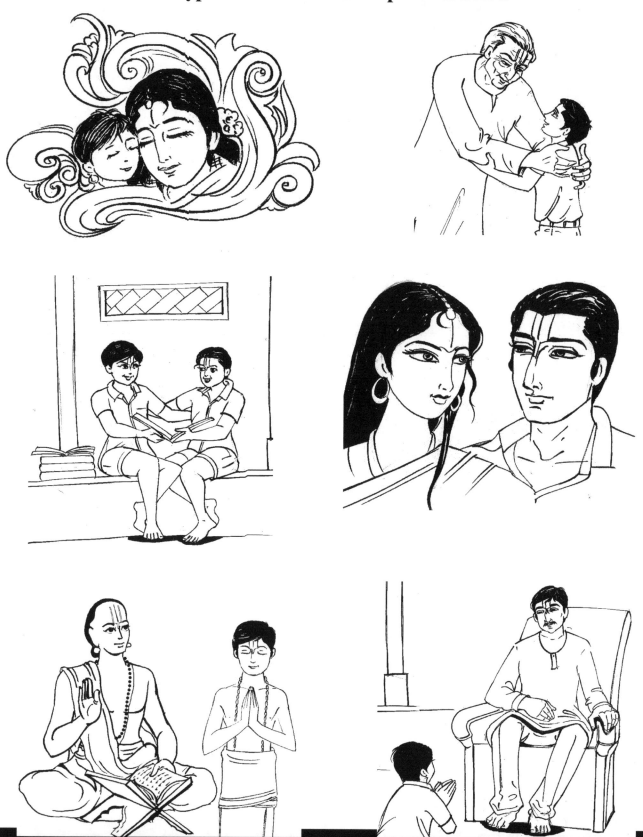

V. Who is a good friend?

Sort the words below and categorize them as what a good friend would do or would not do.

listens to you, shares with you, always agrees with you, hurts your feelings, understands your feelings and moods, solves problems, compliments you, not dependable, respects you, not trustworthy, cares about you, talks about you behind your back, tries to help you when you need help, cheers you up, always agrees with you, always praises you.

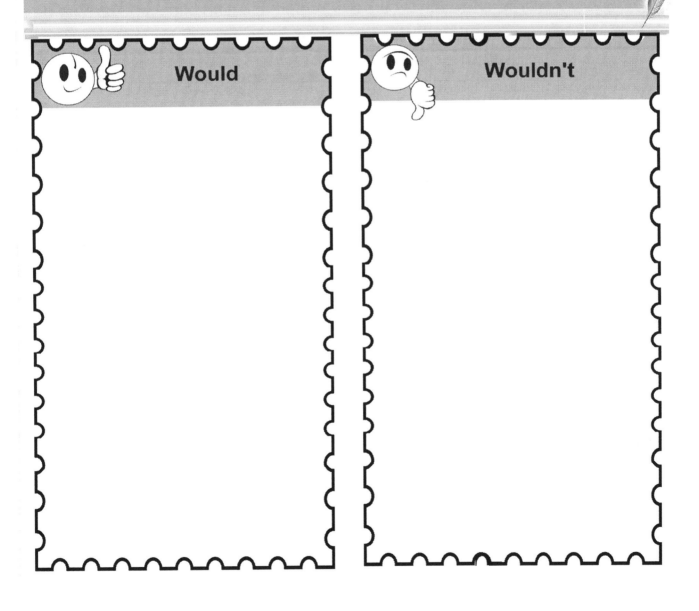

Would	Wouldn't

VI. Sharing corner

1. How did you meet your best friend?

2. Relate an incident where you gave your friend something he wanted without him asking for it.

VII. Illustrate this quote with a drawing

"Friendship with false people is like a clay pot, easy to break but difficult to rejoin. Ideal friendship is like a pot of gold, difficult to break but easy to mend." - Panchathanthra

VIII. Project

1. Take 1/2 cup flour. Place a pinch of it on paper. Blow it. What happens?

   Now mix little water to make it dough. Place it on paper and blow it. What happens?

   Observe that when water is mixed with flour, it brings the flour particles together.

2. Place a wick in a lamp. Fill the lamp with water and light the wick. What happens? Now repeat the above step but put oil instead of water. What happens?

   Observe that both water and oil are liquids but the lamp can be lit with only one of the two liquids. Explain Why? What is this quality called?

Do you know?

v *'asa:dha:rana dharma'* means a unique quality.

v Cohesiveness is the essential quality of liquids. In sanskrit 'Cohesiveness' is called *'snigdhatha/sne:ha'*. In other words, *'snigdhatha/sne:ha'* is the *"asa:dha:rana dharma"* of liquids.

v The word *'sne:ha'* is coined because of its unique attribute i.e *'snigdhatha'*, cohesiveness.

2. FRIENDSHIP SURPASSES STATUS

I. Choose the correct answers

1. A friend always
   a. forgets the other when he is rich
   b. wishes the best for the other
   c. deceives
   d. lives in riches

2. Kuche:la
   a. lived in Dwa:raka
   b. loved pounded rice
   c. was poor
   d. had only one child

3. Krushna
   a. ignored Kuche:la
   b. did not recognize Kuche:la
   c. asked Kuche:la to leave
   d. invited Kuche:la lovingly

4. Lord
   a. gives a devotee everything he requires
   b. Himself carries everything a devotee requires and gives it to him
   c. does not listen to us
   d. is ignorant

5. Kuche:la returned home
   a. contented
   b. unhappily
   c. with a lot of wealth
   d. none of the above

6. Kuche:la took _____ as a gift for Krushna.

   a. a gold ornament

   b. a cow

   c. pounded rice

   d. a laptop

7. 'Whatever he blesses me with will always be good'

   a. shows Kuche:la's devotion for Krushna

   b. shows Kuche:la's passive outlook

   c. shows Kuche:la's indifference

   d. none of the above

8. Krushna sent Kuche:la

   a. with a heavy heart

   b. happily

   c. angrily

   d. along with wealth

9. _____ brought wealth to Kuche:la's house.

   a. Soldiers

   b. Krushna and Rukmini

   c. Krushna and Balara:ma

   d. none of the above

10. Welcoming with Pu:rnakumbha is

   a. a game

   b. inviting a guest with an auspicious pot filled with water

   c. a garland

   d. a nice chair

II. Fill in the blanks

1. Krushna and _____ became close friends.

2. _____ became the ruler of Dwa:raka kingdom.

3. Kuche:la had _____ children.

4. Friendship is _____.

5. Kuche:la's wife invited Kuche:la with _____.

III. True or False

1. The pounded rice was fresh and sweet.

2. Krushna demonstrated the qualities of a true friend.

3. Krushna ate 3 hands full of pounded rice.

4. Kuche:la went back to Dwa:raka to ask for money.

5. Kuche:la went to Nandago:kula.

6. Sathyabha:ma stopped Krushna from eating more pounded rice.

7. Kuche:la and Krushna studied in Ka:si.

8. Krushna felt very happy seeing Kuche:la.

9. It is dangerous to be friends with God.

10. Kuche:la did not recognize his own wife and kids.

IV. Match the following

1. Krushna   a. queen of Dwa:raka

2. Kuche:la   b. ruler of Dwa:raka

3. Sa:ndi:pani   c. classmate of Dro:na

4. Drupada   d. guru of Kuche:la

5. Rukmini   e. classmate of Krushna

V. Who said to Whom?

1. Why do you feel shy?

   _____

2. Enough eating.

   _____

3. How can I repay that now?

   _____

4. Let things happen in their own way.

   _____

5. This is the blessing of God.

   _____

VI. Reorder the pictures as per the story sequence.

☐   ☐   ☐   ☐   ☐   ☐

VII. Who am I?

1. My family was very poor. Sometimes, my siblings and I had to sleep without eating food the whole day. But, one day we suddenly became rich. Who am I?

2. My husband invited a poor man to our house and gave him lot of respect. My husband even ate the smelly, old rice flakes the poor man brought. Who am I?

3. I stopped this poor man from entering the castle. The poor man started telling me stories that he knew the king very well. I did not believe him. Who am I?

4. My owner lent me to her neighbor. My journey began with this poor neighbor and finally ended in the most beautiful Lotus hands. What am I?

5. I am always with the rich people. The poor wish that they had me. But only with the grace of God, I go to them and make them rich. What am I?

VIII. One Word Answers

1. What did Kuche:la offer Krushna?

    _____

2. Who stopped Krushna from eating more pounded rice?

    _____

3. Where did Kuche:la meet Krushna?

    _____

4. Who asked Kuche:la to go to Krushna?

    _____

5. Where did Krushna and Kuche:la study?

    _____

IX. Answer the following

1. Why did Kuche:la go to meet Krushna?

_____

2. Why did the guards stop Kuche:la?

_____

3. Explain "*riktha hasthe:na no:pe:ya:th …*"

_____

4. What forced Kuche:la to meet with Krushna?

_____

5. Explain '*the:sha:m nitya:bhi yuktha:na:m …..*'?

_____

6. What is the beauty of friendship?

_____

7. What did Kuche:la realize on his way back home?

_____

8. Compare friendship shown by Krushna towards Kuche:la to that of Drupada towards Dro:na.

_____

9. What did Lord Krushna give Kuche:la in return for a handful of pounded rice?

_____

10. How did Kuche:la react after reaching home?

_____

X. Imagine you are a scholar.

Write your reaction on meeting an uneducated friend.

XI. What's the Word?

    a. giving nature   G E ___ ___ R ___ ___ ___

    b. Kuche:la looked like a   P E A ___ ___ ___ ___

    c. plentiful   A ___ U N D ___ ___ T

    d. synonym of practice   ___ ___ ___ T O M

    e. opposite of poverty   O ___ U ___ ___ N ___ E

XII. Picture Scramble

Unscramble the pieces & put their labels in boxes

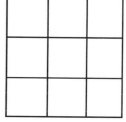

XIII. Word Mine Puzzle

Make as many Sanskrit or English words as possible using the word 'VAHA:MYAHAM'

XIV. Unscramble the tiles to reveal a famous quote on friendship

IS	IEND	A FR	IN	A FR	IEND

EED	IND	NEED

XV. Kuche:la dropped a bag of gold coins. Can you help find 20 'sne:ham', 's' gold coins.

XVI. Double Puzzle

Unscramble each of the clue words. Take the letters that appear in boxes and unscramble them for the final message.

CIRE

RPOO

TINH

ETFE

EIFW

RFIA

KADR

| | U | : | | | | U | M | B | | |

XVII. Find at least 15 differences

XVIII. Color the pictures

Imagine that you are the lion. Write a story to explain what is going on.
What is the moral of the story? Color the pictures.

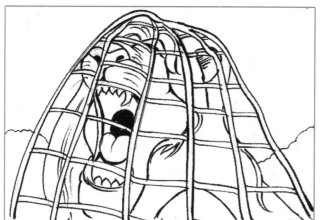

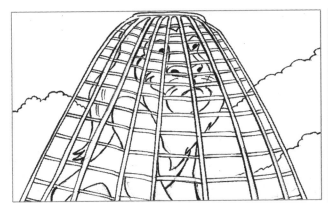

XIX. Draw

1. Pu:rnakumbham

2. the:sha:m nithya:bhi yuktha:na:m yo:ga kshe:mam vaha:myaham

3. riktha hasthe:na no:pe:ya:th ra:ja:nam daivatham gurum….

XX. MAP - Find a path for Kuche:la to go to Dwa:raka

XXI. Let us Learn

Extend your friendship

a) Wherever there is friendship, there is always concern. When our friends need some help, we cannot stop ourselves from extending a helping hand. Friendship can exist between two or more people. It can also extend to the community we live in.

VT Seva is a volunteer organization serving the community. You are the team leader. One of the goals of VT Seva is to provide clean drinking water for remote villages in India. How and what would you do with your team of 30 members to provide potable water?

Help your friends

b) Although Krushna was a king, he did not forget his friendship with Kuche:la. When He saw Kuche:la, He understood the difficulties Kuche:la was going through. Krushna removed Kuche:la's worries by giving him a lot of wealth. We should follow Krushna's example and help our friends.

Your friend Karthik is very worried. His childhood friends are conjoined twins. Now they are 11 years old. To get separated, they need to undergo an operation costing $1,000,000. Karthik wants to do something for them. As a VT Seva Health Coordinator, how can you help your friend?

XXII. How to make good friends?

Rishi and Puja's mother died of cancer. They moved to Houston and joined a new school. Rishi was unhappy to go to a new school.

Questions

1. What made Rishi unhappy?

   _____

2. Why did Rishi walk around with an angry frown on his face?

   _____

3. What helped Rishi to realize that acting 'tough' was not helpful to make new friends?

   _____

4. How did Rishi's behavior change after attending the VT Seva Friends Club at school?

   _____

5. At the end of the story Rishi had a smile on my face.' Explain why.

   _____

XXIII. Project

1. Make a Prajna Sne:ham chain. Watch for instances where classmates exhibit qualities of a friend. Write the student's name and what they did on a paper. Tie the papers to a string, and hand the string from the walls of the Prajna classroom. Make this a year-long activity by attaching friendly qualities to the string, so that a Prajna Friendship Chain is formed.

2. Prepare a delicious dish using rice flakes. Share the recipe your class.

3. Write a poem on 'Friendship' using some of the words below.

   Bend, blend ,end, fend, lend ,mend, send ,spend, tend, trend , amend, ascend, attend ,befriend, commend ,contend ,defend ,depend , descend, extend

XXIV. Research

"*The most I can do for my friend is simply to be his friend. I have no wealth to bestow on him. If he knows that I am happy in loving him, he will want no other reward. Is not friendship divine in this*?" Whose quote is this? To which century and country did the writer belong?

Food for thought and Conclusion

1. Money and social status should not be a barrier for friendship.
2. When a friend is in dire need of help or money, do not hesitate to help him.

Did you know?

* The Kuche:la story is from Srimad Bha:gawatham. It was written by Sage Ve:da Vya:sa. Srimad Bha:gawatham has 18 cantos. This story is from the 'dasama skandha', 10th canto.

* Lord Na:rayana incarnated as Sri Ra:ma. Although Sri: Ra:ma was the king of Ayo:dhya, his closest friend was a tribal, Guha. Sri: Ra:ma called him 'a:thmasamas sakha: (a friend who is equal to my own life).

* Although Krushna is the Lord of the Universe, he became friends with the uneducated cowherd boys and girls. He played with them as if he were one among them. One day Krushna and his friends went on a picnic. They sat in a circle and started exchanging their lunches. The food they brought was not up to the mark. Hence, it was not fit to be offered to God. Yet, Lord Krushna went to each and every boy and tasted their food. All the de:vatha:s and Lord Bramha were shocked watching the scene from the skies. This proves the accessibility of Lord Krushna. He is the greater of the greatest, whereas those boys were lower of the lowest. Krushna gave priority to friendship only and not to the status of his own. Let us try to learn, practice and enjoy His divine bliss!

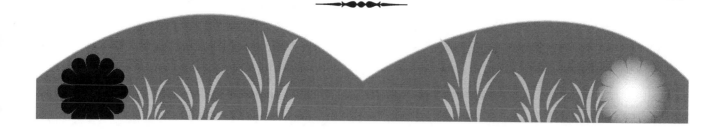

3. EVERYTHING IS FOR GOOD

I. Choose the correct answers

1. The minister always said

   a. "It is for our own good"

   b. "It is our own Karma"

   c. "It is all in God's hands"

   d. "Do not worry, be happy"

2. The bandits needed

   a. a happy man

   b. a wealthy man

   c. a strong man

   d. a wise man

3. The king was upset because

   a. he lost his finger

   b. the minister laughed at him

   c. of the minister's comment

   d. none of the above

4. The minister's approach towards life was

   a. positive

   b. negative

   c. relaxed

   d. none of the above

5. The king went to forest to

   a. hunt

   b. hike

   c. see Nature

   d. meditate

6. The minister gave good advice favoring

    a.   the King

    b.   the kingdom

    c.   a & b

    d.   his relatives

7. After the king returned from forest, he _____

    a.   took rest

    b.   captured the bandits

    c.   released the minister from prison

    d.   paid respects to his parents

8. The bandits left the king because

    a.   he was too fat

    b.   he was missing a finger

    c.   they were scared

    d.   it started to rain

9. Losing a finger proved beneficial to _____

    a.   the king

    b.   the minister

    c.   the bandits

    d.   both a and b

10. Moral of the story

    a.   Take a true friend's statements positively.

    b.   Be positive and think positive

    c.   Never hurt your friends.

    d.   All of the above.

II. Fill in the blanks

1. The bandits practiced _____ to gain evil powers.

2. Sumantha and Subuddhi were good _____.

3. Sumantha lost his thumb in _____ fighting.

4. Bandits captured the king to _____him.

5. King repented for putting his friend in _____.

III. True or False

1. King treated his minister as his subordinate.

2. Doctors gave the king a band-aid for his cut.

3. Bandits in the forest caught the king.

4. The king put his minister in jail for lying.

5. Sumantha and Subuddhi were childhood friends.

6. The king liked Subuddhi's comment.

7. Sumantha lost his thumb in a war.

8. Sumantha was lost in the forest.

9. Subuddhi was unhappy in jail.

10. Sumantha admired Subuddhi's way of thinking.

IV. Who said to whom?

1. 'It is for our own good.'

   _____

2. 'The bandits would have captured me.'

   _____

3. 'I'm really sorry my dear friend!'

   _____

4. 'Are you crazy to say that 'It is for our own good?''

   _____

V. Rearrange Sentences in Order

1. King recollected, "It is for our own good".

2. While going to jail, Subuddhi said, "It is for our own good".

3. Minister told the king, "It is for our own good".

4. While providing first-aid, Subuddhi said, "It is for our own good".

5. After getting released, Subuddhi said, "It is for our own good".

VI. Who am I?

1. We lived in the forest and performed special rituals to gain evil powers. Who are we?

2. I was a part of the royal body. But one day, a sword separated me from the king. What am I?

3. All bad people come and stay here. But one day, a noble person was sent to my place. He stayed here for a long time. What am I?

4. The bandits were very happy. They were drinking and dancing in ecstasy while making strange noises. But, I broke the bad news and spoiled their excitement. Who am I?

5. My friend was very angry at me but later he appreciated me for my positive outlook. Who am I?

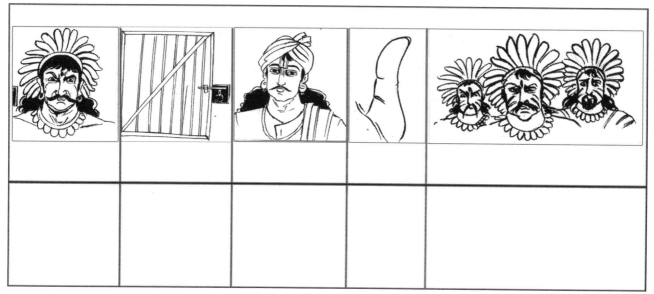

VII. Short Answers

1. Who captured the King?

2. Who put the minister in prison?

3. Where did the King go to hunt?

4. What angered the King?

5. How did Subuddhi respond to his punishment?

6. What was the bandits' reaction to the King's disability?

7. How did the King react to Subuddhi's comment after releasing him from jail?

8. What were the King's feelings on realizing his mistake?

VIII. Answer the following

1. How did the King's loss prove to be a blessing in disguise?

2. Why did the bandits capture the King?

3. How did the bandits prepare the King for sacrifice?

4. What is the moral of the story?

5. Describe an incident in your own life where you felt the 'warmth of friendship'?

IX. What's the word?

1. Call somebody into court   S __ M M __ __

2. Outlaw, a robber   B __ N__ __ __

3. Be sorry   R __ P __ __ T

4. What do we wear   __ __ O __ __ E __

5. Buddy, pal   __ R __ __ N __

X. Picture Scramble

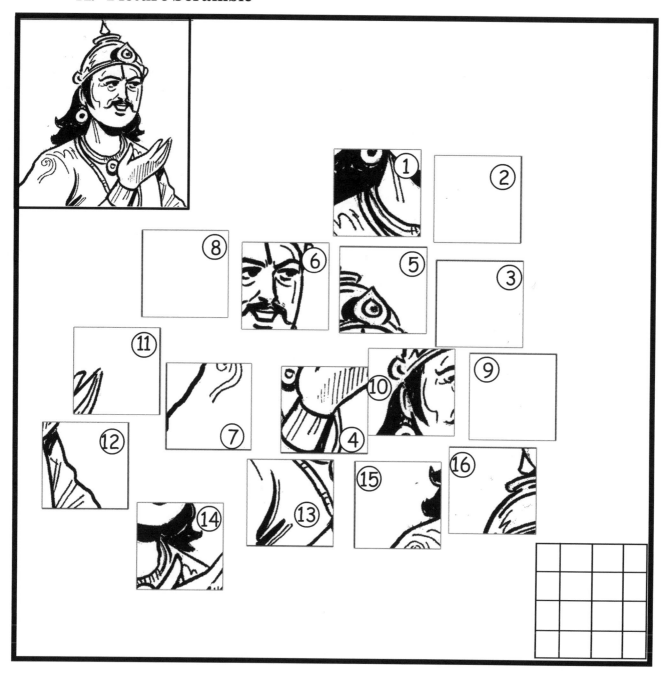

XI. Word mine puzzle

Make as many English words as you can from "FRIENDSHIP".

XII. Unscramble the tiles to reveal a message.

| S | F | R Y T | O R | O O D | N | G | G | I | O W | O U R |

| E V E | H I N |

XIII. **The bandits are riding on horses trying to capture the king. Can you spot 8 horses in the picture below?**

XIV. Picture Story

In olden days, the king and their minister were good friends. The kings always listened to the ministers' advices and both of them worked closely for the welfare of the kingdom. King Krushnade:va Ra:ya and his minister Thena:li Ra:makrushna, shared such friendship. Thena:li often used to give advices to the King and the King always took them in good spirit.

One day, the King's mother fell sick. She summoned the King and said "Dear Son! I wish to eat a mango before I die". It was very tough to find ripe mangoes at that time of year. The King ordered his soldiers to search the entire kingdom for ripe mangoes. They returned with a basket full with them. However, the old lady breathed her last before eating them. Krushnade:va Ra:ya felt very sad for not fulfilling his mother's last wish. So, a few scholars advised the King to donate golden mangoes. The King followed their advice. Day in and day out, long queues lined up outside the palace. The kingdom's gold reserves were getting exhausted

Imagine you are Thena:li Ra:makrushna. Complete the story based on the pictures below.

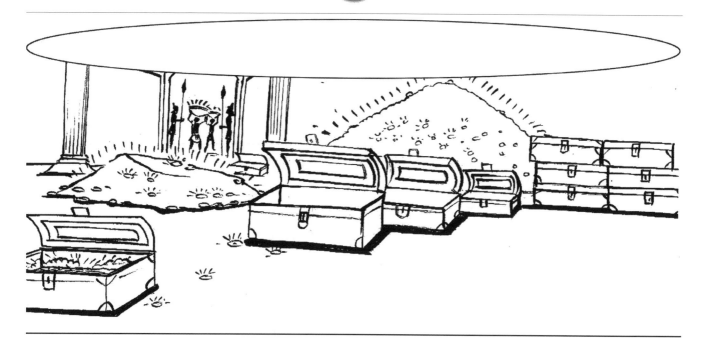

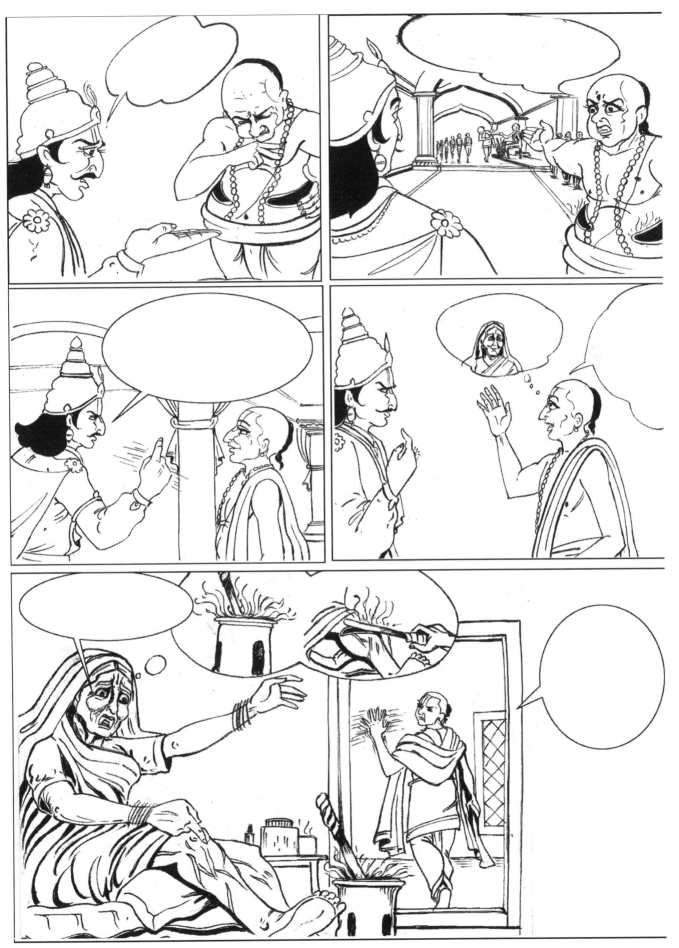

The King realized his foolishness. He appreciated Ra:makrushna's polite suggestion to protect the wealth of the kingdom, as a good friend. Friends always stand guard to their friends not only in protecting them physically, but also in safeguarding their wealth and prestige, without hurting them.

XV. Find atleast 15 differences

XVI. Project

1. **"How to Be a Good Friend"?** Collect pictures on friendship behaviors. Create a classroom collage gathering everyone's pictures in your Prajna class.

2. Collect your friends' opinions about yourself in a scrapbook.

3. Brainstorm a list of rules for "How to Be a Good Friend" in your Prajna class. Display the list in your classroom. Periodically discuss and add new rules to the list as needed.

4. What do you think are your friends' opinions of you?

XVII. Research

a) Who quoted the following?

1. "The best mirror is an old friend."

2. "What is a friend? A single soul in two bodies."

b) Find out examples from our history where a king and his minister were good friends.

XVIII. Comprehension - Qualities of a Good Friend

Puja always had a smile on her face. Her classmates started talking to her. Soon, she became everyone's friend. She became the VT Seva Friends Club Trainer. Rishi attended one of her classes to understand how a good friend behaves.

Is kind to animals and younger kids

Follows school rules and does not try to talk you into breaking rules, stealing, cheating, lying etc

Avoids gossiping

Always respect others and is loyal to other friends
Happy for you when you get good grades or something good happens to you

Questions

1. "To have good friends, you must be a good friend." Explain this statement.

   _____

   _____

2. Why should you pick a person with good qualities as a friend?

   _____

   _____

XIX. Let us learn

Listen to Friend's advices

The advice of a true friend might be difficult to accept. However, if such advice is accepted with an open mind, it will eventually benefit us.

a) Your friend joined a neighboring school and fell into bad company. He started picking up bad habits. What would you do to show him the right path?

b) VT Seva volunteers are volunteering in a juvenile home as teachers. They have a specialized curriculum to teach kids subjects such as ethical decision-making, basic hygiene, the dangers of addiction, anger management, relationship management, confidence building, technology and career counseling. If you are given a chance to volunteer, Which topic would you like to teach? Why?

XX. Draw

1. Sports which require teams.

2. Sports which are played by a single player.

3. Sports which can be played in teams as well as by a single player.

XXI. Subha:shitham – Words of wisdom in Sanskrit

pa:pa:th niva:rayathi, yo:jayathe: hitha:ya,
guhya:n nigu:hathi, guna:n prakati:karo:thi |
a:pad gatham cha na jaha:thi, dada:thi ka:le:,
san mithra lakshanam idam pravadanthi santhaha ||

Bharthruhari Subha:shitham

The wise men said-

"A good friend prevents you from committing sins; prompts you to do good deeds; conceals demerits; highlights the merits; does not desert you in distress and renders help in crisis"

Food for Thought

A real friend is closer than anyone in the world.
God's greatest gifts from God ever blessed on humanity is A TRUE FRIEND.

4. TRUE FRIENDS LIVE FOR EACH OTHER

I. Choose the correct answers

1. The search for Si:tha De:vi was postponed
   a. by four months
   b. due to monsoon season
   c. as Ra:ma wanted Sugri:va to enjoy royal pleasures
   d. all of the above

2. Ra:ma chopped the _____ of Kabandha.
   a. hands
   b. legs
   c. ears
   d. nose

3. Vibhi:shana was
   a. Ra:vana's brother
   b. Ra:ma's friend
   c. Thrijata:'s father
   d. all of the above

4. Choose the correct statement
   a. Dundubhi's dead body landed 8 yo:janas away
   b. Ra:ma chopped 7 Sa:l trees
   c. Ra:ma climbed Mt. Rushyamu:ka
   d. none of the above

5. Ra:ma, Sugri:va and their army surveyed Lanka
   a. from top of the mountain
   b. from Pushpaka Vima:na
   c. from Hanuma:n's shoulders
   d. none of the above

6. Ra:ma killed Va:li

   a. with one arrow

   b. from behind a pillar

   c. because he was Ra:ma's enemy

   d. all the above

7. When Sugri:va saw Ra:vana

   a. he leapt towards him

   b. he hid behind Ra:ma

   c. he got angry

   d. a and c

8. Hanuman was _____ Sugri:va

   a. an enemy to

   b. a friend and minister to

   c. master of

   d. none of the above

9. Ra:ma and Sugri:va pledged friendship

   a. with Lakshmana as a witness

   b. with fire as witness

   c. with rain as witness

   d. with Nature as witness

10. One who does not act in haste, thinks properly, sends the right person for a job is a true

   a. friend

   b. leader

   c. janitor

   d. clerk

II. Fill in the blanks

1. Be a good _____

2. Va:li and _____ fought for more than a year.

3. Ra:ma pledged _____ to Sugri:va.

4. Va:li was able to punch one _____ tree at a time.

5. Ra:ma shot _____ trees with a single arrow.

6. Ra:ma observed austerities on Mount _____.

7. Ra:ma crowned Sugri:va as king of _____.

8. Following Kabandha's advice, Ra:ma reached the banks of River
   _____.

9. Va:nara:s constructed a _____ .

10. Ra:vana used _____ _____ to
    subdue Sugri:va.

11. Sugri:va was enjoying the company of _____ and
    _____.

12. _____ advised Ra:ma to meet Sugri:va.

13. Hanuma:n found Si:tha in _____

14. _____ sought refuge at the feet of Ra:ma.

15. A leader is equivalent to the_____ of the body.

III. True or False

1. Sugri:va broke his promise to Ra:ma.

2. Good friendship overlooks self pride.

3. Initially, Sugri:va did not have qualities of a good friend.

4. Ra:ma accepted Vibhi:shana's friendship hesitantly.

5. Sugri:va doubted Ra:ma's strength.

6. Kabandha asked Ra:ma to meet Hanuma:n.

7. Hanuma:n introduced himself to Ra:ma as the king of Kishkindha.

8. Va:li was Ra:ma's enemy.

9. Ra:ma kicked Dundubhi's dead body into the air.

10. Friendship should be reciprocated.

IV. Match the relationships

1.	Kabandha	a.	brother of Sugri:va
2.	Sugri:va	b.	brother of Ra:ma
3.	Hanuma:n	c.	king of apes
4.	Va:li	d.	demon
5.	Dundubhi	e.	minister of Sugri:va
6.	Lakshmana	f.	wife of Sugri:va
7.	Tha:ra	g.	brother of Ra:vana
8.	Ruma	h.	uncle of Ra:vana
9.	Ra:vana		
10.	Ma:ri:cha		
11.	Vibh]i:shana		

V. Match the following places with their significance

1.	Panchavati	a.	River
2.	Rushyamu:ka	b.	Kingdom of Va:naras
3.	Pampa:	c.	Sugri:va's hiding place
4.	Kishkindha	d.	Ra:vana kidnapped Si:tha
5.	Mount Ma:lyava:n	e.	City of Ra:vana
6.	Lanka	f.	Ra:ma observed austerities here

VI. Who said to Whom?

1. "Don't lose heart like that!"
2. "We shall share our joys and sorrows equally from now on."
3. "He thought that I plotted his death."
4. "He knows every corner of this world."
5. "That path still remains open."

VII. Rearrange Sentences in Order

1. Va:li and the demon Dundubhi entered a cave while fighting.
2. Kabandha advised Ra:ma to get help from Sugri:va.
3. Va:li immediately lost his temper and banished Sugri:va.

4. Ra:ma told Sugri:va about the abduction of Si:tha.

5. Ra:vana kidnapped Si:tha.

6. Ra:ma pledged friendship with Sugri:va.

7. Ra:ma said, " You returned safely. Good God! Nothing happened to you"

8. Sugri:va waited outside the cave for one and a half years.

9. Hanuma:n met Ra:ma and Lakshmana on the banks of river Pampa.

10. Sugri:va leapt towards Ra:vana and started punching him.

VIII. Who am I?

1. We are four brothers. My eldest brother has strange friends – a monkey, a ra:kshasa, a tribal etc. Who am I?

2. I am a very huge monster. I have no head. I have very long hands. My one eye and my huge mouth are on my trunk. Who am I?

3. My owner is awesome. If he sends me to do a job, I complete it successfully, purify myself by entering the earth and then return to my home which my owner carries on his back. Who am I?

4. I am very sacred and am used in various religious occasions. Some time ago, a lotus eyed man and a Va:nara pledged friendship in my presence. Who am I?

5. I was a demon with a bull face. I challenged a monkey and lost my life. Once, soft lotus like feet kicked my skeleton high into the air. Who am I?

6. I am a bird. I fought against the ten headed demon to save a lady who was being kidnapped. Who am I?

7. One day, I challenged my elder brother. The first time we fought, I was beaten up black and blue. I ran away. Who am I?

8. I sometimes became a vehicle and carried Ra:ma and Lakshmana on my shoulders. Even now, in temples, I carry the Lord on my shoulders. Who am I?

9. Land was our home. But, these va:nara:s, threw us in the ocean and since then we have been floating in the water. Ocean became our home. Who are we?

10. I am a ra:kshasa. I have two younger brothers. One of them supported me but the other deserted me and joined the enemy. Who am I?

IX. Short Answers

1. Where was Sugri:va hiding?

   _____

2. Who helped Ra:vana?

   _____

3. Who turned into an angel?

   _____

4. To which race did Sugri:va belong?

   _____

5. Name the brother of Sugri:va.

   _____

6. Where did Ra:ma spend his 12 years of exile?

   _____

7. Who was familiar with every nook and corner of the world?

   _____

8. How did Ra:ma reach the peak of Rushyamu:ka?

   _____

9. How many sa:l trees could Va:li cut at a time?

   _____

10. From whom was Sugri:va hiding?

    _____

11. Where did Ra:ma meet Hanuma:n?

    _____

12. How long did Sugri:va wait for Va:li outside the cave?

    _____

13. Who found Si:tha in Lanka?

    _____

14. When did Sugri:va come to his senses?

    _____

15. What prevented Va:li from climbing Mt. Rushyamu:ka?

    _____

16. Who closed the entrance of the cave?

    _____

17. Whom did Ra:ma send to give a stern warning to Sugri:va?

    _____

18. What did Ra:ma want from Sugri:va?

    _____

19. Who noticed Ra:vana first?

    _____

20. In which direction did the armies go in search of Si:tha?

    _____

X. Answer the following

1. Describe an incident which shows Sugri:va's immense love for Ra:ma.

    _____

    _____

2. Describe Sugri:va's grief while narrating his sad story.

    _____

    _____

3. Explain Ra:ma's friendship with Sugri:va.

   _____

   _____

4. How did Ra:ma console Sugri:va?

   _____

   _____

5. Why was Va:li angry with Sugri:va?

   _____

   _____

6. Why did Ra:ma make sure that Sugri:va kept his promise?

   _____

   _____

7. What did Ra:ma promise Sugri:va?

   _____

   _____

8. What are the qualities of good friendship?

   _____

   _____

9. Why did Sugri:va leap towards Ra:vana?

   _____

   _____

10. How many pairs of siblings do you see in this story? Compare their relationships.

   _____

   _____

XI. What's the Word?

1. To show   D E __ O __ S __ R __ T __
2. Overjoy   E L ___ T ___ D
3. Grief   S __ R __ O __
4. Rest   R __ L ___ X
5. Hit   PU___ ___ H

XII. Picture Scramble

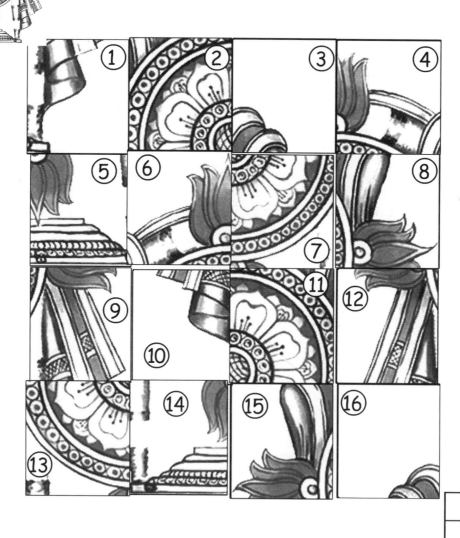

XIII. Word Mine Puzzle

Make as many English and Sanskrit words as you can from "SARANA:GATHI".

XIV. Unscramble the tiles to reveal a famous quote on friendship

ST	M I R	B E	AN	OL	ROR	ND	D F
IS	R I E	T H E					

XV. Sort the pictures as per the sequence of the story. Also, name the characters in the pictures.

XVI. **Draw the trail of Ra:ma's journey from Panchavati to Lanka and his return journey to Ayo:dhya.**

XVII. **Complete the story**

Friends have a good understanding amongst themselves. They listen to each other as they know that their friend's advice is always beneficial. Friendship brings unity. Unity makes them strong. They achieve whatever they want. Once, a flock of doves lived on a tree. Dove Raj was the king of the birds. Though Raj was the King, he was very friendly with his subjects. One day...................

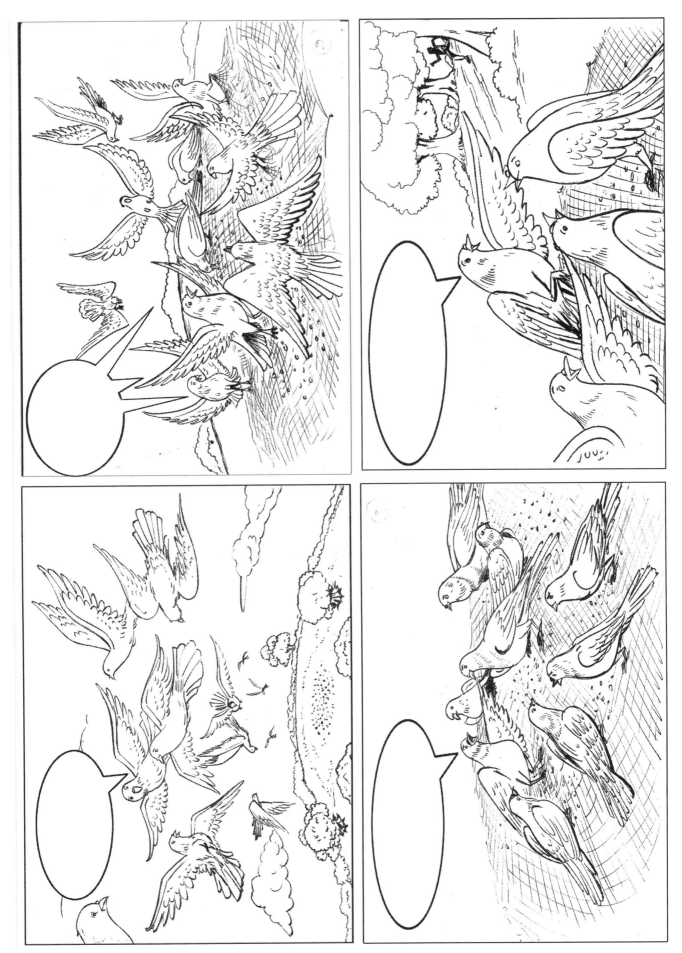

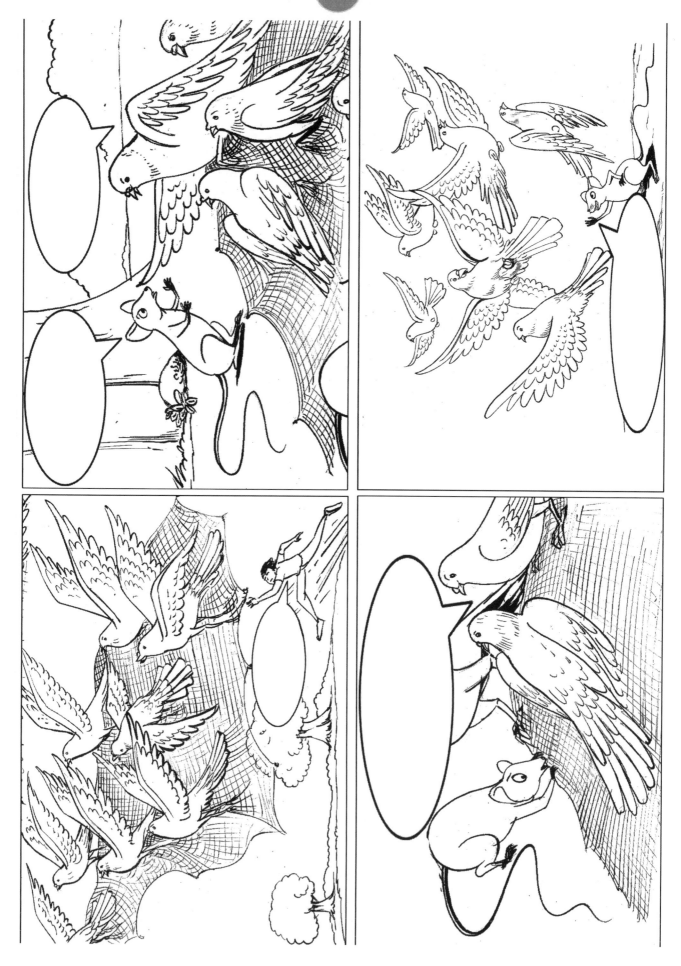

XVIII. Find atleast 15 differences

XIX. Write a Story - I need a Friend

XX. Let us Learn

Be a good team player

Ra:ma and Sugri:va were going through a very difficult phase in their lives. Sugri:va was driven out of the kingdom by his brother Va:li. Ra:ma was also separated from Si:tha by Ra:vana. After Ra:ma and Sugri:va pledged to be good friends, they decided to stand guard for each other and get rid of their troubles. Ra:ma helped Sugri:va become the king of Kishkindha and, of course, Sugri:va also helped Ra:ma in finding Si:tha. Thus, as friends, they joined their efforts, worked as a team, and thus benefitted.

Joint efforts are always more fruitful compared to a single man's effort. Hence, learn to work in a team. Be a good team player. Success will be yours.

You are a VT Seva Volunteer Lead. What would you do as a team leader to form a VT Seva team to help in a relief activity?

XXI. Draw

1. Kabandha

2. Va:nara:s building Nalase:thu

3. Ra:ma's arrow breaking 7 sa:l trees

4. Ra:ma kicking Dundhubhi's skeleton

5. Sugri:va punching 10 headed Ra:vana

XXII. Project

1. Create an advertisement with the title 'Need a Friend'.

   Write the qualities, hobbies, favorite activities you are looking for in a friend.

2. Write a poem on how Sugri:va attacked Ra:vana.

XXIII. Research Activity

1. Location of 'Nala Se:thu' the oldest man made bridge. Collect the pictures taken by NASA satellites.

2. There are a few remains of the Ra:vana's fort in Sri Lanka where Mother Si:tha was kept hostage. Collect some pictures and write few words about it.

3. "It is easy enough to be friendly to one's friends. But to befriend the one who regards himself as your enemy is the quintessence of true religion. The other is mere business."

   ⁻ Who quoted this? To which country did he belong? What is his full name?

XXIV. Subha:shitham – Words of wisdom

ja:ni:ya:th pre:shane: bhruthya:n ba:ndhava:n vyasana:game: |
mithram cha:padi ka:le: cha bha:rya: cha vibhavakshaye: ||

A servant's faithfulness is revealed during the time of necessity. Relatives are they, who support during difficult times. <u>Friends are they, who protect in times of danger</u> and wife's love is known in times of losing wealth and status.

Did you know

v   This story is from Ra:ma:yana. Ra:ma:yana is an Ithiha:sa written by Sage Va:lmi:ki. It is the first recording of historical events, and also the first poetic composition of mankind.

v   Ra:ma:yana has 24,000 slo:kas. Ra:ma:ya na has 7 parts called ka:ndas. They are Ba:la Ka:nda, Ayo:dhya Ka:nda, Aranya Ka:nda, Kishkindha: Ka:nda, Sundara Ka:nda, Yuddha Ka:nda and Uththara Ka:nda.

v   Sri Ra:ma:yana is the history of a model human being i.e Sri: Ra:ma. Listening to or reciting Sri Ra:ma:yana will bring prosperity.

5. UNPARALLEL FRIENDSHIP

I. Choose the correct answers

1. Sri Ku:re:sa was a _____

   a. renowned scholar

   b. businesman

   c. scientist

   d. vedic priest

2. Ku:re:sa's wife was

   a. Go:da

   b. Lakshmi

   c. A:nda:l

   d. Yaso:da

3. Ku:re:sa gave away his_____

   a. cattle

   b. wealth

   c. house

   d. all of the above

4. Ku:re:sa was _____than Ra:ma:nuja:cha:rya.

   a. younger

   b. knowledgeable

   c. handsome

   d. older

5. Who accompanied Ra:ma:nuja:cha:rya to study Bramhasu:thra:s?

   a. Vaduganambi

   b. Ku:re:sa

   c. Maha:pu:rna

   d. Ghoshttipu:rna

6. Bodha:yana Vruththi was available at
   a. Lakshmi Bhanda:r in Kashmir
   b. Pa:rvathi Bhanda:r in Kashmir
   c. Ma:tha Bhanda:r in Kashmir
   d. Saraswathi Bhanda:r in Kashmir

7. Ku:re:sa met Sri Ra:ma:nuja:cha:rya in the city of
   a. Ka:nchi:puram
   b. Sri:rangam
   c. Sri:ku:rmam
   d. Thirumala

8. Ku:re:sa wanted to become
   a. a friend of Ra:ma:nuja:cha:rya
   b. a disciple of Ra:ma:nuja:cha:rya
   c. a disciple of Bo:dha:yana
   d. a friend of Bo:dha:yana

9. Ra:ma:nuja:cha:rya treated Ku:re:sa as a
   a. disciple and friend
   b. disciple only
   c. friend only
   d. none

10. Ra:ma:nuja:cha:rya moved from Sri:rangam to Me:lkote
    a. because Ku:re:sa was in Me:lkote
    b. because of Cho:la king's threats
    c. because Bo:dhayana Vruththi was in Me:lkote
    d. because there was a drought in Sri:rangam

II. Fill in the blanks

1. Ra:ma:nuja:cha:rya accepted Ku:re:sa as a _____ wholeheartedly.

2. Ku:re:sa lived in _____ village.

3. Ra:ma:nuja:cha:rya wanted to write a commentary on

   _____

4. Ve:da Vya:sa composed _____

5. _____is quintessence of Ve:dantic philosophy.

6. Ku:re:sa and Ra:ma:nuja:cha:rya were allowed only _____ days to read and examine the Bo:dha:yana Vruththi scripture.

7. Ra:ma:nuja:cha:rya's commentary on Bramha Su:thras is called

   _____.

8. The Cho:la king was jealous of _____ and decided to kill him.

9. Ku:re:sa did not enter Lord's temple to keep his association with

   _____.

10. _____ and _____ were arrested by the king.

III. True or False

1. Kure:sa became the disciple of Ra:ma:nuja:cha:rya.

2. Cho:la King captured Ra:ma:nuja:cha:rya and ill treated him.

3. Ku:re:sa lost his eyesight while protecting Sri: Ra:ma:nuja:cha:rya.

4. Ku:re:sa asked for his eye sight from the Lord.

5. Ra:ma:nuja:cha:rya was unhappy seeing Ku:re:sa blind.

IV. Match the following

1. Ku:re:sa   a. Author of Sri: Bha:shyam

2. Sri: Ra:ma:nuja   b. Ra:ma:nuja:cha:rya lived here for 12 years

3. Cho:la King   c. Disciple of Sri: Ra:ma:nuja

4. Maha:pu:rna   d. Ra:ma:nuja lived here

5. Me:lkote   e. Plucked out Ku:re:sa's eyes

6. Sri:rangam   f. Guru of Sri: Ra:ma:nuja

V. Who said to whom?

1. "Oh! Wise One! Please dictate the text of the commentary."
2. "Oh Lord! Bless me with divine sight."
3. "What did you ask God?"

VI. Reorder the pictures as per the story sequence and describe the picture.

VII. Who am I?

1. I composed Sri: Bha:shyam along with Ku:re:**sa**. Who am I?

2. I am a disciple of Sage Ve:da Vya:sa and composed an explanation on Bramha Su:thras. Who am I?

3. I am the smallest object in the Universe. I move from one body to another. Who am I?

4. My disciple's disciple and I were winning the debates in Ve:dic subjects. The king got jealous and removed my eyes. Who am I?

5. I was a treasure house. Lot of scriptures were taken care of in my place. Once a monk and a disciple came to my place to study "Bo:dha:yana Vruththi". Who am I?

VIII. Short Answers

1. Who was Bo:dha:yana?

   _____

2. What did Bo:dha:yana compile?

   _____

3. Who was Ra:ma:nuja:cha:rya's guru?

   _____

4. Who are nithyasu:ri:s?

   _____

5. Where did Ra:ma:nuja:cha:rya stay for 12 years?

_____

6. Whom did the king want to arrest?

_____

7. Who pretended to be Ra:ma:nuja:cha:rya?

_____

8. Which scripture was in accordance with Ve:da Vya:sa's idealogy on Bramha Su:thras ?

_____

9. Who held the debate to establish the supreme reality of the Universe?

_____

10. Where did Ra:ma:nuja:cha:rya and Ku:re:sa write the commentary?

_____

IX. Answer the following

1. How did Ra:ma:nuja:cha:rya test the memory power of Ku:re:sa and why?

_____

_____

2. Define the quality of soul and explain.

_____

_____

3. Why did the guards of Sri:Rangana:ttha temple stop Ku:re:sa from entering the temple?

_____

_____

4. How did Maha:pu:rna and Ku:re:sa save Ra:ma:nuja:char:ya?

_____

_____

X. Picture Scramble

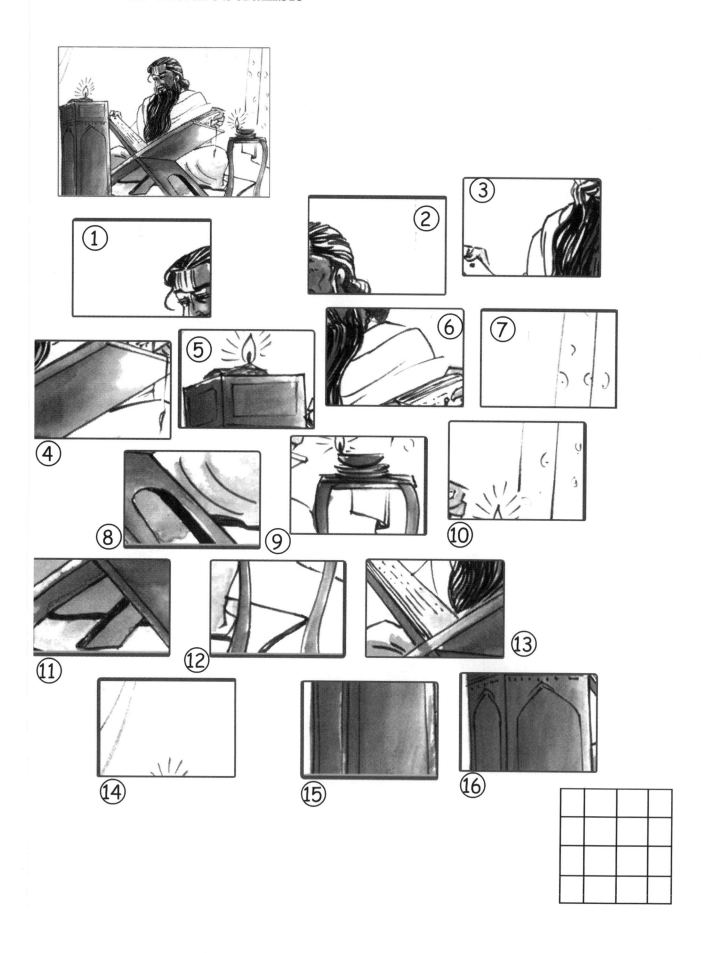

XI. Word Mine Puzzle

Make as many English and Sanskrit words as you can from
"se:shathwe: sathi jna:thruthvam a:thmano: lakshnam".

XII. Unscramble the tiles to reveal a famous quote on friendship

U R S	I V E	E L F	Y O	A F	I S	I F T	N D

R I E	U G	A G	Y O

XIII. Bhagawad Ra:ma:nuja:cha:rya is trying to find the "Bo:dha:yana Vruththi" in Saraswathi Bhanda:r. Can you help Him find it?

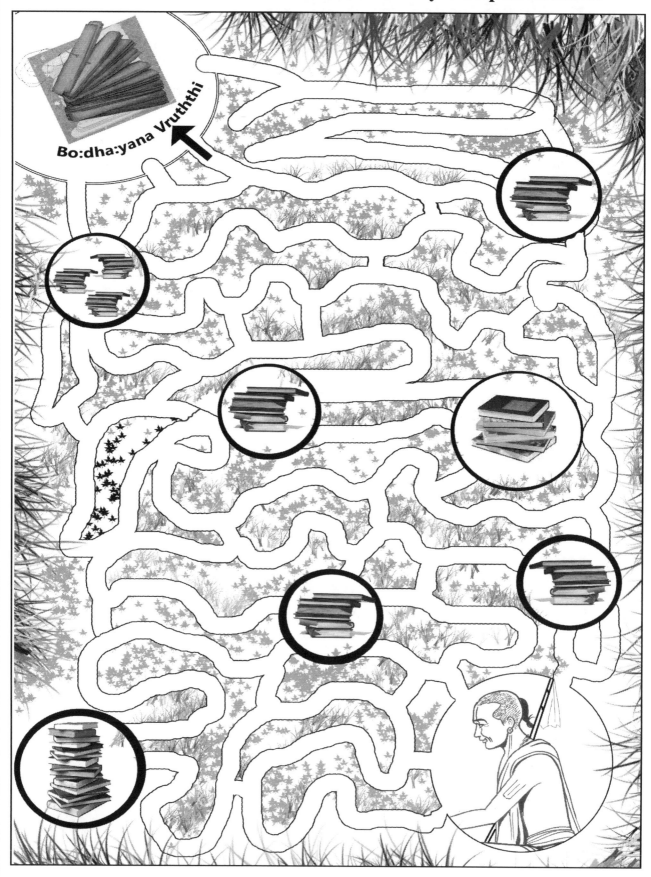

XIV. Explain the difference between the following statements:

Quality of Soul = knowledge along with servitude

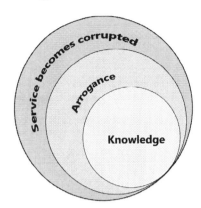

Quality of Soul = servitude along with knowledge

XV. Workshop

How would you deal with this situation

Questions

1. Your best friend was deliberately left out. How did you feel? Why?

   _____

   _____

   _____

2. Why was Roma not invited to the party?

   _____

   _____

   _____

3. Would you let Roma know about the party? If you decide to go to the party, how would you make sure that Roma is not unhappy about it.

   _____

   _____

   _____

4. If you decided not to go to the party, explain why.

   _____

   _____

   _____

5. Should friendship be based on popularity? Why or why not?

   _____

   _____

   _____

6. What should be the base for friendship?

   _____

   _____

   _____

XVI. Let us Learn

To be successful in life, one should be sound in body, mind and soul. To be physically healthy, one should exercise and eat good food. To be mentally healthy, one should have control over their sense organs and manas (thought process). To grow spiritually, one should seek guidance from elderly people. One should make good friendship for overall development in all the three areas.

First, treat your body as a friend. Keep your body in a good condition without others' pressure or force. If you love your own body then, you should inculcate good bodily habits by exercising.

There are multiple ways of doing exercises. Among all, Yo:ga is proved to be more effective in not only keeping the body fit for all activities, but also in increasing our memory power, focusing our thought process to achieve our goals and intellectual progress. Thus it helps us succeed in our life.

VT Seva is conducting a yo:ga boot camp for one week. Design the curriculum.

Manas -Treat your manas as your friend

Not only should you make friends with other people, but you must also befriend your manas, as instructed by Chha:ndo:gya Upanishad. Befriending your manas is the only way you can control your senses and develop increased concentration. Chha:ndo:gya Upanishad gives us an anecdote on how to control your manas.

For example, there is a person who has a bird with beautiful wings in his possession. He longs to see it fly and wonder at its beautiful wings. If the bird is caged, then the beauty is hidden. However if he lets it go, the bird will fly away and never comes back. To solve this problem, he ties a long string to the bird's leg. The bird can fly freely to a great distance enabling him to see its wings but it will always come back to him because of the string. Similarly, if your manas is wandering, don't fight to bring it back. Just like the bird, allow it a little freedom tying it with a strong string, and then slowly coax it into coming back to you. Here, 'aspiration to achieve targets' is the string.

VT Seva is conducting a meditation camp for three days. Give the class tips on how to concentrate.

Be friend to your own self-

Seeking guidance from experienced people is called Sathsang. Associating yourself with good people and becoming friends with them is always beneficial. You will not only develop a good personality but also become more spiritual. You will gain a vast amount of knowledge. Sathsang will not only help you achieve personal goals, but also helps in reaching the main goal of life, 'Serve all beings as service to god.'

How do you decide whether a company is good or bad? Can you recollect some activities of good company from your previous Modules?

XVII. Serve all beings as service to God

Ra:ma:nuja:cha:rya was an ocean of knowledge. Thousands of students learnt scriptures from him. He was not only a big mobile library, he also made his disciples great encyclopedias of different subjects. In those days, they depended on their memory power. They shared knowledge by word of mouth or oral tradition.

On the contrary, today we totally depend upon external sources such as books, CDs, internet etc. A place where all this material is preserved is a library.

Imagine you are the VP of VT Seva. The county is rebuilding the library. They contacted you and assigned you the job of packing 25000 books based on the genre. How would you plan to lead and finish the assigned task with your team of 25 members?

XVIII. Identify Ra:ma:nuja:cha:rya's stay at various places in sequential order based on the stories you read so far on Ra:ma:nuja:cha:rya in A:cha:ryadevo: bhava and Sne:ha.

XIX. Draw

1. Ra:ma:nuja:cha:rya's thridandam and pa:duka:s.

2. Saraswathi Bhandar

XX. Project

1. Write a "Friendship Cake" recipe. Use cooking vocabulary and measurements such as dash, sprinkle, tablespoon, etc for this recipe. For ingredients, use words showing friendly activities. Document the steps to make this cake. Example – Add a dash of loyalty before mixing the dough.

2. Draw how your Friendship cake looks and decorate it.

XXI. Research

Who quoted these famous quotes? To which period and country did they belong?

1. "So long as we love, we serve; so long as we are loved by others, I would almost say that we are indispensable; and no man is useless while he has a friend."

2. "A friend is someone who knows all about you and still loves you."

XXII. Subhashitham – Words of wisdom in Sanskrit

uthsave:, vyasane: chaiva, durbhikshe:, ra:shtraviplave: |
ra:jadva:re:, smasa:ne: yas thishttathi sa ba:ndhavaha ||

"He who stands by your side during good times, bad times, droughts, war, famine, riots, in court and during the final journey of life, is a true friend."

Did you Know?

v Bhagawad Ra:ma:nuja was born in 1017 and lived for 120 years.

v Bhagawad Ra:ma:nuja had 5 gurus. 1. Maha:pu:rna – gave ashta:kshari: di:ksha, 2. Go:shtti:pu:rna – revealed the secret of Charama Slo:ka, 3. Sri:sailapu:rna – taught secrets from Sri Ra:ma:yana , 4. Thirunaraiyu:r Arayar – taught Tamil scriptures called Divya Prabandhas and 5. Thiru Ma:lai A:nda:n – gave the commentaries of Divya Prabandhas.

v Ra:ma:nuja:cha:rya considered another great person also as his guru who quenched his thirst by answering 6 questions. That guru was Ka:nchi:pu:rna/ Thirukkachchinambi.

v Bhagawad Ra:ma:nuja revealed the Ashta:kshari: Manthra, the king of all manthras to all, irrespective of their caste or creed

v Ashta:kshari: Manthra talks about

     *   Who am I?

     *   Who is the Supreme God?

     *   Our relationship with Him.

v Because he wrote an outstanding commentary, Sri: Bhashyam on Bramha Su:thras, He was conferred the title "Bha:shyaka:ra" by Goddess Saraswathi.

v Bhagawad Ra:ma:nuja propogated a doctrine called Visishta Advaitha based on Ve:das.

v The Holy Ve:das say that there are 3 Realities - God, Soul and Nature. Nature changes its form and attributes. Soul doesn't change its form but attributes change. Whereas with God – there is no change in His form or attributes.

v Bhagawad Ra:ma:nuja's physical body is seen even today, well preserved in Sri:rangam temple, using natural herbs and oils.

6. FRIENDSHIP IS GOOD EVEN WITH GOD

I. Choose the correct answer

1. Kulase:khara was a staunch devotee of
   a. Siva
   b. Durga
   c. Na:ra:yana
   d. Indra

2. Kulase:khara considered Ra:ma as his _____
   a. Father
   b. God
   c. Friend
   d. all of the above

3. Su:rpanakha was the sister of
   a. Ra:ma
   b. Ra:vana
   c. Si:tha De:vi
   d. none of the above

4. We have
   a. 12 a:lwa:rs
   b. 13 a:lwa:rs
   c. 15 a:lwa:rs
   d. 10 a:lwa:rs

5. Khara was
   a. Su:rpanakha's brother
   b. Ra:vana's sister
   c. Ra:ma's friend
   d. none of the above

II. Fill in the blanks

1. Kulase:khara ruled the kingdom of _____.

2. Milk gives water its _____ and _____.

3. Ra:ma asked _____ to guard Si:tha while he fought with Khara.

4. The scholar narrated _____ .

5. True friends cannot tolerate being _____from one another.

6. Kulase:khara was called a _____.

7. Kulase:khara was eager to serve _____ .

8. _____ knew the King since childhood.

9. True friends never _____to help each other.

10. Si:tha embraced Ra:ma out of _____.

III. True or False

1. Kulase:khara stopped getting ready for war after hearing about Ra:ma's victory.

2. Ra:ma cut the ears and nose of Su:rpanakha.

3. Kulase:khara was scared hearing Ra:ma was alone.

4. Si:tha tried to harm Su:rpanakha.

5. Kulase:khara was a great devotee.

IV. Who said to Whom?

1. "God! You should never tell the King any scenario in which Ra:ma faced troubles."

2. "Bring me my armor and helmet immediately."

3. "Hail to the king!"

4. "Let the army rest now."

V. Who am I?

1. I was very beautiful. I fell in love with Ra:ma and Lakshmana. But the younger brother cut off my nose and ears. Who am I?

2. My king was very good, but sometimes lost sense of time due to his friendship with Ra:ma. I always had to be attentive and make sure the king did not get excited hearing the story of Ra:ma. Who am I?

3. I went with a huge army of 14,000 demons to fight against Ra:ma. Who am I?

4. I was a king of Kerala. Because of my staunch devotion towards Lord Vishnu, I became an a:lwa:r. Who am I?

5. I love my friend very much. No one can separate us. Sometimes fire tries to separate us but is not successful. Who am I?

6. My friend was in great danger. He was all alone fighting against a huge army of 14,000 demons. I ordered my army to get ready to help my friend. Who am I?

VI. Short Answers

1. What did Kulase:khara hear everyday?

   _____

2. Whom did Kulase:khara invite?

   _____

3. How did Si:tha react after Ra:ma defeated the 14,000 soldiers?

   _____

4. Who tries to come between the friendship of milk and water?

   _____

5. What is the term used to describe the nature of friendship?

   _____

VII. Answer the following

1. What did Kulase:khara do after hearing that Ra:ma was attacked?

   _____

   _____

2. Describe 'kshi:ra ni:ra nya:yam'. How does it relate to friendship?

   _____

   _____

3. How does a true friend behave?

   _____

   _____

4. Explain 'Friendship is good even with God'.

   _____

   _____

5. When did Kulase:khara ask the army to rest?

   _____

   _____

VIII. What's the word?

1. Another word for devotee   BHA ___ T __ __

2. Synonym of fuss, disturbance   C __ MM __ T __ __ N

3. Synonym of money   ___ E A __ T ___

IX. Picture Scramble

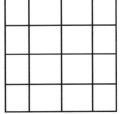

X. Word Mine Puzzle

Make as many English and Sanskrit words as possible using letters from 'kshi:ra ni:ra nya:yam'.

XI. Unscramble the tiles to reveal a message

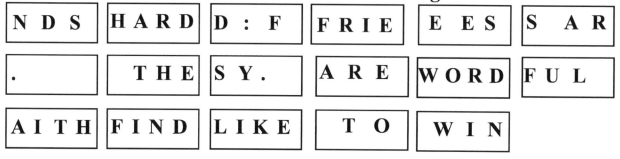

N D S	H A R D	D : F	F R I E	E E S	S A R
.	T H E	S Y .	A R E	W O R D	F U L
A I T H	F I N D	L I K E	T O	W I N	

XII. King Kulase:khara is searching for his sword to get ready to fight against Khara. Can you help find it for him?

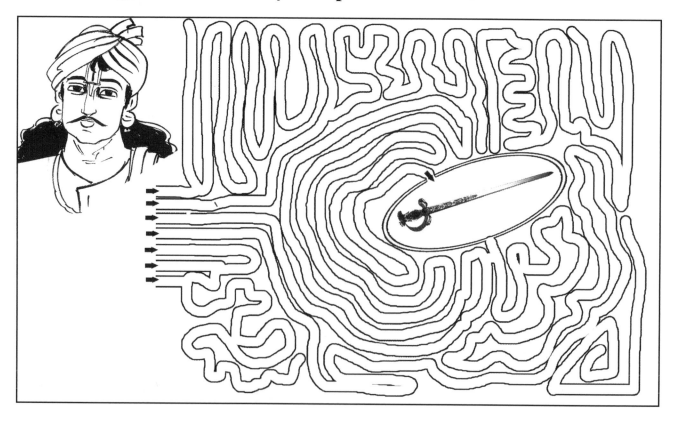

XIII. Find atleast 15 differences

XIV. **Imagine that a good friend of yours moved to Switzerland. She/He would like to hear from you. Write him or her a letter about why you miss him or her and the good times you used to have together.**

XV. Write up

Friends- Things I would do for a friend

XVI. Let us Learn

Be a friend of Nature

· A good friend always feels bad when the other is passing through difficult times. He feels the same pain and experiences the sufferings that the other friend is going through. Ra:ma was friendly with all beings. Hence, when Ra:ma was leaving Ayo:dhya, all the citizens felt very sad. Even Nature felt sad. Seeing the difficulties of Ra:ma, the lush green trees withered. The water in the ponds and rivers started boiling. Thus even Nature responded to Ra:ma's hardships because he loved them all.

* Sakunthala loved and treated plants as if they were her best friends. She spent her whole childhood amongst the trees, talking to them and taking good care of them. When Sakunthala was leaving the a:sram of her father Sage Kanva, all the plants felt very sad. They could not bear the separation. The plants gave her a warm send off by bending low and showering flowers on her with love.

* Be a friend of Nature. Nature will reciprocate. Do not exploit Nature. We are committing many atrocities by squeezing Nature's resources. Hence, Nature unable to bear the pains, is showing its anger and agony in the form of earth quakes, tsunamis, droughts, famine, hurricanes etc.

  You are VT Seva Team Director. Plan and implement a rescue effort to help the tsunami victims by providing immediate and long term relief.

2.

XVII. Illustrate the story in pictures

Two cats – Kitty and Fatty were close buddies. Once, they stole a huge block of cheese. While cutting it into half, they started fighting with each other. Kitty blamed Fatty that it was taking the bigger piece, while Fatty denied it. Their fight continued for long. Meanwhile a monkey came, saw that two friends were fighting and volunteered to help them. Tricking them that it will give them equal share, it kept on cutting the cheese into pieces, pretended to weigh them both in two hands and then ate one piece declaring that the other was huge. Soon, the monkey ate the whole cheese and ran away. Kitty and Fatty realized their mistake. They decided not to fight with each other in future. They also decided not to involve any third person in between.

What is the moral of the story?

XVIII. Project

1. Interview your parents and family members about their childhood best friends. Collect their pictures and glue them in your scrapbook.

2. Ask your parents to tell you about their friendship that changed or ended because their friends moved, or became part of a different group, etc,. How did they feel then?

3. Ask your family members to describe a time when they met their old friend in a School Reunion and were surprised as the old friend was different from what they expected him to be.

4. Make a Friendship bracelet and give it to one of your Prajna friends.

XIX. Research

1. Who quoted the below famous quotes? To which period and country did they belong?

    a) "Friendship is born at that moment when one person says to another: "What! You too? I thought I was the only one."

    b) "Good friends, good books, and a sleepy conscience - this is the ideal life."

    c) "Am I not destroying my enemies when I make friends of them?"

    d) "Words are easy, like the wind; Faithful friends are hard to find."

2. "sarvattha: sukaram mithram dushkaram paripa:lanam" 'making friends is easy, but, maintaining them is too difficult a task' said Ra:ma in Sri Ra:ma:yanam. To which period did he belong?

3. What happens if neighboring countries are friendly? What happens if the neighboring countries are enemies?

4. Write the advantages of all the nations being friendly with each other.

5. Research and list the countries that are friends. Also list the countries that are enemies.

Do you know?

As human beings, our resources are limited. Yet, we can extend our help to our friends in our own way. We might feel like doing a lot when a friend is in need. But, we don't need to restrain ourselves because of our limited resources. Remember the saying 'Aim for the stars. Even if you miss, you will land on the moon.' Start planning to help in a big way. God will provide you with all the resources.

God is all powerful. He is the Master of the Universe. His wealth is unlimited. That Supreme Lord appeared as Sri Ra:ma and extended his hand of friendship towards us. He declared thus -

mithrabha:ve:na sampra:ptham na thyaje:yam katthamchana |
do:sho: yadyapi thasya sya:th satha:m e:thad agarhitham ||

I promise to protect anyone who befriends me. He does not need to come as a true friend, even if he pretends to be a friend and seeks my protection, even if he is a great sinner, I will still protect him. Wise people will accept it.

Let us become friends of Lord Ra:ma now itself and enjoy His love and protection.

YOGASANAS

CHAKRA:SANAM

Breathing the air in (Inhale)

1

Exhale

2

A:sana
Stthithi

3   Inhale

4   Exhale   (Hold for a while, and
                  then keep take normal
                  breath)

5   Inhale

6   Exhale

7

Inhale

8

Exhale & A:sanastthithi

VRUSCHIKA:SANAM

A:sana Stthithi

1   Breathing the air out (Exhale)

2   Inhale

3   Exhale

4   Inhale   *(Hold for a while, and then keep take normal breath)*

5   Exhale

6   Inhale

7   Exhale

8   Inhale & A:sanastthithi

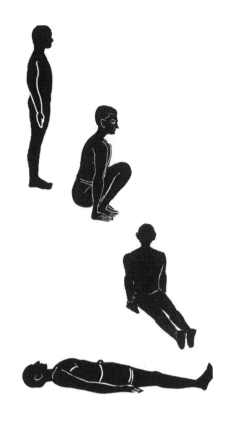

PLAVA:SANAM

A:sana Stthithi

1   Breathing the air in (Inhale)

2   Exhale

3   Inhale

4   Exhale   *(Hold for a while, and then keep take normal breath)*

5   Inhale

6   Exhale

7   Inhale

8   Exhale & A:sanastthithi

PAVANA MUKTA:SANAM

A:sana Stthithi

1   Breathing the air in (Inhale)

2   Exhale

3   Inhale

4   Exhale   *(Hold for a while, and then keep take normal breath)*

5   Inhale

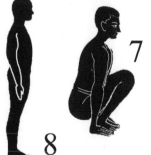

6   Exhale

7   Inhale

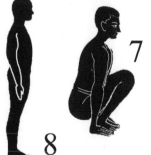

8   Exhale & A:sanastthithi

BADDHAPADMA:SANAM

A:sana Stthithi

1 Breathing the air in (Inhale)

2 Exhale

3 Inhale

4 Exhale *(Hold for a while, and then keep take normal breath)*

5 Inhale

6 Exhale

7 Inhale

8 Exhale & A:sanastthithi